JOHN MORRISON is still trying
he feels his talents deserve. He was convinced he was
onto a winner with *The Satanic Pulses: a Vegetarian
Cookbook* - which hoped to exploit the worldwide
success of Salman Rushdie's seminal work. That was
until a spineless publisher pulped every copy and fled
to Bolivia on a forged passport.

Then came *Feng Shui for Beginners*: an introduction
to what we used to know, more prosaically, as 'tidying
up'. His most recent work - *Women are from Venus,
Men are from Mytholmroyd* - throws light on some
of the more puzzling aspects of the gender war. With
a back catalogue like this, can that elusive best-seller
be far away?

He now lives in Hebden Bridge, with the usual roster
of regrets and neuroses. Happily, life in the South
Pennines has proved wackier - and the people far
more eccentric - than anything he could possibly
invent for his books of dubious humour.

View from the Bridge - what they said

"Local publishers Pennine Pens beat all records with a runaway
local hit" - The Book Case

"I'm not giving publicity to someone who slags me off. He can
go hang" (Sheila Tordoff, editor of the *Hebden Bridge Times*).

"I rather think Hebden Bridge is going to have a good laugh at
itself" (Sir Bernard Ingham).

"Better than Tolstoy..." (Vic Allen, *Artscene*).

Published 1998 by Pennine Pens
Copyright © John Morrison 1998
All rights reserved

ISBN 1 873378 52 1

Dedicated to the bankers at NatWest, without whom the writing of this book would have been a hell of a lot easier.

Typeset and published by Pennine Pens.
32, Windsor Road, Hebden Bridge,
West Yorkshire, HX7 8LF. Tel/Fax 01422-843724
books@penpens.demon.co.uk
http://www.hebdenbridge.co.uk

BACK TO THE BRIDGE

John Morrison

Pennine Pens

CONTENTS

Introduction

View From the Bridge was published in Spring 1998. Since it didn't promise to "change your life" or offer the prospect of instant weight loss, we confidently expected it to sell a few dozen copies and then sink without trace. In the nick of time the book was given a helpful leg-up in the publicity stakes by being banned by the local press. Word-of-mouth did the rest, and the first imprint sold out so quickly that we soon had to reprint. Bizarrely, we found we had a minor hit on our hands...

The editors of the *Hebden Bridge Times* and *Halifax Evening Courier* seemed disturbingly quick to identify with the book's mildly unflattering portrayal of a fictional newspaper. "He's writing about a crap local paper," they seemed to be thinking, "he must mean *us*"... They may have banned my little book, but the antagonism is not reciprocated. I read every issue of the *Hebden Bridge Times* from cover to cover, and can confidently say that those five or six minutes are the highpoint of my week.

There was even an anonymous poster campaign against the book. Fair enough: if you put your head over the parapet and take pot-shots, you expect to get a few bullets in return. You just like to know who's firing them. The observation that I was "a rather sad and friendless figure" suggested that the writer was someone who knew me only too well.

If you hold up a distorting mirror to a small community, it's startling to discover how many people will imagine that they recognise themselves. Memorably, one or two stock characters even 'came to life' and turned up on our doorsteps. Craven apologies have kept us out of trouble thus far, and the libel writs have failed to materialise. Nevertheless, the people in the book are merely caricatures, and the least savoury aspects of their imaginary personalities are mostly mine...

View From the Bridge was received pretty well. Most folk seemed to find it funny, which is all it was ever meant to be. A few people suggested it was a bit cynical. Yet, when it comes to cynicism, I'm a mere novice when compared with, say, the editors of our tabloid newspapers, the entire advertising profession or the fat-cat bosses of the privatised utilities. I'm not in the least bit cynical about the important things in life: love, affection, friendship, loyalty and, of course, cricket.

I prefer to think of the book as an affectionate view of a small Pennine town, and an idiosyncratic population that fairly buzzes with creative talent. I came to live here by choice, and it feels very much like home. If the prose is a bit sour on occasions... well, the male menopause can be a difficult time...

The book's success has emboldened me to knock out another slim volume. The formula is much the same as before: jaundiced observations about stereotypical characters... sniping at predictable targets... undemanding stuff, really, just shooting fish in a barrel. So let's go *Back to the Bridge* for another whistle-stop tour of familiar terrain...

From the beginning these episodes have been 'published', week by week, on the internet. It's been pointed out to me that this isn't a particularly innovative thing to do. I totally agree: it's just one more way for a writer to find an audience. What's new about the internet is that the audience can write back. It's great fun to get responses from people all around the globe who, despite the welter of salacious material available in cyberspace, still find the time to check out the Milltown Web and see what's happening at the Bridge.

Episodes old and new will continue to be available on the Milltown Web, an entertaining and pioneering example of what can be achieved when a small community goes on-line. Just point the browser at...

http://www.hebdenbridge.co.uk

Or email me at **john@trunorth.demon.co.uk**

John Morrison

A Time of Waste

There's not a lot happening in Milltown. We're in that briefest of interludes between the end of the January sales and the arrival of the Easter bunny. The streets are almost empty. Maybe it's a flag-day. Maybe the neutron bomb's gone off. Maybe it's just half-day closing.

It seems like a good time for Milltown folk to tackle those tedious but essential little jobs. Our Town Drunk is videoing the weather forecast ("Well, you never know...", he says, enigmatically). Willow Woman, slapping some paint on the back-bedroom ceiling, is suddenly overcome by emulsion. The landlord of the Grievous Bodily Arms, Milltown's own den of iniquity, has just been diagnosed as suffering from Miserable Bastard Syndrome. Expecting a busy night he's watering his beer, with an expertise that comes from years of practise. Dope Dealer is attempting to snort a line of talcum powder through a counterfeit fiver; he can't seem to do *anything* right at this time of year.

Our beleaguered Tourism Officer is sucking the end of his pencil. His brow is furrowed; his job is on the line. He's been told to dream up a slogan so bland and meaningless that it will attract visitors in droves. So today's news-flash - that there are to be performance league tables for abattoirs - comes as a heaven-sent opportunity for him to make Milltown a major tourist magnet.

He consigns his thoughts to paper in an excited scribble. He's thinking: interactive. He's thinking: multi-media. He's thinking: lottery funding. Start with an urban farm where kids could pet the baby lambs... Then follow 'their' lambs through the whole fascinating slaughterhouse process... Finally (and our Tourist Officer's hand is shaking with the sheer brilliance of his ideas), serve lunch at the carvery next door: roast lamb, mint sauce and all the trimmings. An unforgettable day out for all the family.

In contrast, Wounded Man is staring morosely out of his kitchen window. The view is curtailed by the rotting pile of half-eaten kebabs in his front garden: the result of living too near the Milltown Take-away. It's not a pleasant sight, and even the hungriest of rats would think twice before having an exploratory nibble. Their diet - shit, mostly - precludes eating something with as little nutritional value as a kebab. Wounded Man, aware it's time for action, orders up a rubbish skip.

But there's a protocol attached to this simple act about which he is wholly ignorant. He doesn't know that it's actually a sophisticated recycling system, proving that one man's rubbish is, indeed, another man's treasure. The hiring of a skip is a tacit invitation for his neighbours to indulge in what has become a traditional, two-part ritual.

Step one: wait until the attention of the skip-hirer has been momentarily distracted. In the few seconds it takes to tie a shoe-lace, or redistribute the contents of a pair of over-tight Y-fronts, there is just enough time for doors to open and for neighbours, laden down with unwanted possessions, to tip-toe purposefully towards Wounded Man's little house. When he turns around to look at the skip again, Wounded Man does a deadpan double-take of the kind that a white-faced Buster Keaton all but patented. The last door is closing, noiselessly, and the skip - his skip - is filled to overflowing with other peoples' detritus.

Step two of the ritual is conducted at a more leisurely pace. Over the next couple of days, his neighbours give the contents of the skip a cursory examination as they walk past, followed, under cover of darkness, by furtive forays to liberate perfectly serviceable stuff that others have so thoughtlessly thrown away. There's wood to burn. And a chair: a perfectly fine chair that will look as good as new after a lick of paint. And that old radio: it probably only needs fresh batteries...

And so it continues. By day three the skip will be almost empty once again, allowing Wounded Man to load it with the malodorous contents of his front garden. It's been a novel experience to partake in this quaint urban ritual; next time he hires a rubbish skip he'll know what to expect.

Flights of Fancy

It's the middle of January. For the good people of Milltown - busy shovelling snow, jump-starting obstinate cars and shivering at bus-stops - spring looks a very distant prospect indeed. Town Drunk, disorientated by flu and an unpredictable cocktail of cleaning fluids, staggers into the chemist. With a hot water bottle filled with Lemsip, he feels confident of getting a good night's sleep. When, at the first sign of a sniffle, Willow Woman asked the chemist to make something up for her, he said there were fairies at the bottom of his garden. It's this sort of facetious remark that has made her resort to homeopathic remedies in future.

The Smallholder family is leaving the rain-drenched streets of Milltown far behind, to enjoy a much-needed winter break in some sun-kissed, malaria-ridden, Caribbean holiday haven. They're flying to Taramasalata, blissfully unaware that it's not a real resort at all... but just a name made up for spurious comic effect.

The Smallholders travel first-class - or better - whenever they fly. This would make every sense if the first-class surcharge trimmed a few hours off the flight time. But, of course, it doesn't. The people travelling in sub-economy class - the very people the Smallholders have spent a small fortune to get away from - reach their destination at exactly the same time. This infuriates Mr Smallholder who feels that, on arrival, the package-holiday riff-raff should be incarcerated on the plane for a few extra hours, to wipe the upholstery down and collect the sick-bags.

The airline bosses, aware of these inconveniently egalitarian arrival times, know they can't really make first-class travel any more luxurious. The glamorous hostesses already cater to the first-class passengers' every whim ("More champagne, sir? A blowjob?") so the easiest way to widen the gap between the classes is to make life in the cheap seats totally unbearable.

The budget passengers aren't served with meals; all they get is a pot snack apiece and a kettle to share. All their in-flight films feature violent plane crashes. The piped music consists entirely of Chris de Burgh

9

concerts. Once the drinks have been spiked with laxatives, the toilet paper is heartlessly removed. The hostesses don't bother to demonstrate how to inflate a life-jacket, in case of an emergency, because there aren't any hostesses in sub-economy class... and there aren't any life-jackets either. In any case, how reassuring is it for passengers to be told: "In case of an unscheduled landing on water, your life-jackets are stowed under your seat". At the risk of being pedantic, you don't *land* on water... you plummet fatally from a great height.

Bizarrely, it takes more than this kind of maltreatment to subdue the high spirits of the passengers in sub-economy class. They usually have a spontaneous round of applause once the plane has landed safely, and organise a whip-round for the pilot.

Dreams of Avarice

It's reassuring for Wounded Man to read that there might actually be - as he's often imagined - a gene for bad luck. It's intriguing to conjecture that his straitened circumstances might be due to the fickleness of fate rather than his own financial ineptitude.

Like so many other Milltown folk he's taken the decision to resign from the rat-race and the ceaseless striving for promotions and bonuses. He refuses to be defined merely by the work he does, and by the acquisition of meaningless status symbols. In the process he has rendered himself virtually unemployable. Now, following the Christmas festivities (which included such extravagant treats as a 20lb turkey-shaped nut-roast) he's running a fore-finger down the columns of figures on his bank statement. He may not be very good with numbers, but there's no getting away from the unpalatable truth: Wounded Man is broke.

There was a time when your bank manager was an avuncular man, with a firm handshake and a reassuring manner, who dispensed advice and comfort from an impressive oak-panelled office. There was a sense - however illusory - that his role in life was to help his customers navigate the choppy waters of their personal finances, by giving advance warning of rocks and icebergs.

He would be prepared, when necessary, to deliver a measured speech of mild reproach to his more feckless customers, on those occasions when their ship appeared to be rudderless. But he'd leave you with a friendly pat on the shoulder and the certainty that you'd take his words to heart. He was a man you felt you could trust. Together with the vicar and the family doctor, the bank manager made up a secular trinity of irreproachable professionals. But those days, alas, are long gone.

These 'old school' bank managers have been hastily ushered out of their offices and into early retirement, to spend their declining years trimming their roses and listening to Gilbert and Sullivan operettas. The bank staff of today are a very different kettle of fish. Sharks, in a word: cruising dangerous waters in search of the luckless and unwary. Waiting to see fear in their customers' eyes, ready to attack.

It is into this cut-throat world that Wounded Man enters on Monday morning: an innocent abroad. He is ushered into an office the size of a broom cupboard, furnished with a table, two chairs and a desk lamp. The only decoration is a framed Hogarth print, one of a cautionary series extolling 'The Pleasures of Usury'.

Wounded Man's simple request - a small overdraft until his ship comes in - is greeted with hollow laughter from the Lending Officer, a woman who would give Edwina Currie a run for her money in an Edwina Currie look-alike contest. "You don't seem to understand", she says, icily. "The bank's policy is to deny overdraft facilities to those of our customers who can prove beyond reasonable doubt that they actually *need* one. Once we see that life has become difficult for you, we feel it is our responsibility to ensure that it becomes absolutely impossible".

Wounded Man sits open-mouthed: a stunned mullet confronted by a basking shark. "So you won't be able to help me..." "Certainly not", she replies, snapping her briefcase shut with a finality that seems to preclude further discussion. "On the contrary I will give you until next Friday to get your account back in credit. Otherwise I will dispatch two of our most unpleasant bank tellers - and, believe me, some of them are *very* unpleasant indeed - to your squalid little house. Then, if you can't pay - in cash, in full - they will be authorised to chop off your bollocks and use them as a table decoration. I bid you good day".

He reels out of the door in confusion. Since he doesn't drink at the Grievous Bodily Arms or watch Eastenders, Wounded Man is unaccustomed to this sort of language. How can he possibly find the money so quickly? His usual response to trouble - adopting a foetal position and whimpering - can do nothing to postpone the appalling prospect of being emasculated with a rusty machete.

Drastic problems require drastic solutions, so Wounded Man thinks seriously about selling one of his organs. A brochure from the Burke 'n' Hare Transplant Clinic puts flesh on the bare bones of an unsavoury trade. They specialise in celebrity organs: from the sublime (Cliff Richards' todger, "as new", apparently) to the ridiculous (Oliver Reed's liver, offered free, without guarantee, to anyone who can give it a good home). He notes that they buy organs for cash, with generous part-exchange deals... just nano-seconds before he wakes up, bathed in sweat, to realise that this chapter has been a bad dream. Yeah, that's it. Just a bad dream.

One Man and his Doggerel

The literati of Milltown greet the publication of Ted Hughes's new collection of poems with a collective dropping of the jaw. It's hard to recall when poetry landed with such a resounding thud on the doormat of our imaginations. Love him or loathe him (and he seems to inspire strong feelings either way) we feel a little proprietorial about our 'local boy made good'. Strange, then, that a polite enquiry in the bookshop elicits a puzzled response from the new assistant. "Ted Hughes? Nah, he doesn't work here any more".

Never mind, there are plenty of folk in Milltown who need no prompting to ruin an otherwise pleasant evening in the pub by announcing, portentously: "I'd like to read a poem". Let's not mince words: writing poetry is the art of saying in two finely-honed words what might have been better expressed in twenty. Whining about the iniquities of life, in faltering verse, is something you do in adolescence while your skin clears up. If the urge continues long after the discovery of masturbation and shoot-'em-up computer games, best see a doctor. And, like masturbation, poetry is best performed without an audience, in the privacy of your bedroom. Think very hard before attempting it in public. Then wash your hands.

Willow Woman writes poems about what it's like to be a poet, and the problems of being so sensitive in a world that doesn't care. It's not easy being a poet. Hacking through the dense undergrowth of her innermost thoughts, fears and desires can be a traumatic business. Even something as simple as finding a scrap of paper and a pencil stub can be a morning's work in a household where chaos rules.

We have Bill Gates and his ilk to thank for demystifying the printing process, and making it available to anyone with a computer and a laser printer. The good news: it's now possible for anyone to publish a slim volume of poetry. The bad news, conversely, is that it's now possible for *anyone* to publish a slim volume of their poetry. And then force those precious pages into the reluctant hands of family, friends and neighbours - most of whom, if given the choice, would prefer to be flicked remorselessly with a wet towel than to waste their leisure hours reading poetry.

Willow Woman's own little collection of verse is not something you'd want to read twice. It's not something you'd want to read even *once*, to be honest, but a promise is a promise. Having been entrusted with her first literary efforts, Wounded Man is turning the pages without enthusiasm. "You'll tell me what you *really* think, won't you?" she had said, meaning nothing of the kind. A born diplomat, happy to offer a meaningless platitude when necessary, he's already wondering what to say to her. Some faint praise that will bring a smile to Willow Woman's lovely, ingenuous face, yet give her not the slightest encouragement to consign any more of her maudlin poems to paper.

Farming the Fells

L ife can be hard above the tree-line, where the Smallholders have their palatial ranch. It's not particularly arduous for the Smallholders themselves, of course, whose idea of farming, according to their more truculent neighbours, is keeping "a couple of sheep and six fucking honey bees".

Theirs is an ostentatious spread that, architecturally speaking, puts two fingers up to the workaday farmsteads that surround it. You can tell it's not a 'real' farm because there aren't any rotting animal carcasses, rusting farm machinery or savage dogs, chained up and half-crazed from howling at the moon. The gates work; the farmyard is suspiciously tidy; a polished Range Rover is parked where a clapped-out tractor ought to be. Instead of the all-pervading, sinus-clearing stench of slurry, you may recognise - if the windows are open - the more agreeable aroma of pot-pourri, furniture polish and money.

The hill farmers of Yorkshire have a reputation for dour taciturnity and stubborn intransigence. It's a reputation that's both deserved and hard-won, and they'll be buggered if they'll change their ways to accommodate a bunch of soft, southern bed-wetters like the Smallholders. The farmers get up at dawn. They go without holidays. They work all hours God sends, and a few more besides. Arduous work is their currency; it's what they understand best. Without hard, menial, unrewarding work their lives would lose all meaning. The farming community has its own skewed internal logic, and a deeply conservative nature that abhors change. So what gets them angry, *really* angry, is people like the accursed Smallholders, who just *play* at being farmers.

Hill farming is a way of life that should, by rights, have died out years ago. One by one the more isolated farms around Milltown were abandoned, as life at these altitudes became insupportable. Families locked up their farmhouses, cast tearful glances back to what their ancestors had worked so hard to built up, vowed to return one day... but never did. The towns had need of millhands, and soon claimed them.

Empty farms, full of ghosts, haunt the higher fells; for years you couldn't give them away. Then came the Smallholders - and others like them - squealing with delight at the thought of converting these gaunt gritstone ruins into bijou residences. Every time a farm is sold to overpaid townies, the farmers shudder with a mixture of envy and dread. Selling up is the last resort. It's crushing to be the one who has to bring a family's farming dynasty to an inglorious end, with the finality of an on-site auction held under grey and gloomy skies. It's not a decision to be taken lightly.

People talk about the inevitability of change. You can't stand still, say the Smallholders. It's not that we're against change, but why do things always have to change for the *worse*?

The Sporting Life

The Winter Olympics, currently taking place in Japan, have a distinctly ambivalent place in our affections. Scoring very heavily on the 'who gives a flying fuck?' factor, the event is failing to set Milltown buzzing with enthusiasm. It takes someone very bored (our Town Drunk, for example) to care who wins the two-man luge, the biathlon (yeah, skiing and shooting: what a handy combination of skills) or, yawn, curling.

It would be different, of course, if there was any likelihood of Brits winning medals. But there isn't. It's disheartening to think that in a few years time we'll look back to the golden age of British success in winter sports, when Eddie the Eagle tried ever so hard to break his neck on the ski jump. But Eddie has hung up his skies for good, so all we've had to look forward to is the first crop of competitors in Nagano to test positive for drug-taking.

Today we have the poor sap: an American snowboarder who smokes cannabis. Cannabis? This is a drug that has traditionally enhanced the ability to lie on a pile of scatter cushions, listening to Pink Floyd on a pair of headphones, and snacking on crisps and sweets. Rather than sliding down a mountain on an elongated tea-tray. If cannabis is such a performance enhancing drug, then why wasn't Timothy Leary a sporting colossus? The snowboarder insists he has never smoked dope, but just hangs around with a lot of people who do. So maybe it's true: we really *do* judge people by the company they keep.

Our Town Drunk, impressed by this notion, idly wonders whether it's possible for beer, too, to pass from one person to another, by a process of osmosis. Next time he's up at the Grievous Bodily Arms he'll try to wedge himself between a couple of heavy drinkers. It's worth a try.

He's been watching the ski jumping on TV. With the ever-present possibility of competitors wiping themselves out in dramatic fashion, this is one of the few winter sports that engages his attention. Ski jumping is also the sport that presents most problems for the drug-testers, such as how to get the competitors *down*. TV pictures show dozens of stoned Norwegians circling the skies - like buzzards in skin-tight Lycra. It's a remarkable sight.

Town Drunk zaps the channel changer. Rugby: now *that's* more like it. A proper game, played by real men. Being split conveniently into league and union means that fans have not just one incomprehensible game to enjoy, but two. The crowd applauds whenever a player kicks the ball out of play; they'll cheer to the rafters if he manages to clear the stadium altogether and deposits the ball into the next postal district. Baffling.

The uninitiated may see just a bunch of blokes lying in a muddy pile on the halfway line. But if they think that rugby is just an organised punch-up, they are missing some of the game's subtle nuances. They won't understand the sheer poetry of a vicious tackle. They'll fail to appreciate that after eighty minutes of unremitting violence the players will walk off the pitch hand in hand and enjoy a relaxing bath together. And there's that wonderful sense of sportsmanship that rugby engenders. A player who, only minutes before, was trying to gouge his opponent's eyes out in the scrum, will offer to buy him a beer once they're in the bar.

Perhaps rugby can best be seen as a metaphor for life. Since our attempts to go forward are constantly being thwarted by relentless opposition, we are forced to fling the ball backwards. So, after a career of pointless struggle and unfulfilled ambitions, when the hooter of life finally brings the whole messy business to a halt... we find, to our disgust, that we've got absolutely nowhere.

We know all about ear-biting in Milltown. And we don't much like it. The town's rugby team - dubbed the Milltown Marauders - has strict and unequivocal guidelines about this most cowardly of activities. Any player who bites another player's ear will be sent off the field of play in disgrace... and won't be allowed back on until he's finished eating it.

Rugby has at least given the landlord of the Grievous Bodily Arms a legitimate outlet for his most vindictive tendencies. He's left his mark on the game over the years, and on quite a few players too. This season he pulled a hamstring muscle; fortunately it wasn't his.

Compromise or Bust

The anti-war vigil in Milltown has had a startling and unforeseen effect: Saddam Hussein has decided to throw in the towel as a tyrannical dictator, and try his hand instead as a stand-up on Baghdad's emergent comedy circuit.

So it's celebratory drinks all round in the pubs of Milltown. Except at the Grievous Bodily Arms, of course, where the regulars were looking forward to watching the war live on satellite TV, whenever there wasn't any football on. An uncritical audience, they'd have been happy if Gulf War II had repeated some of the finest cinematic moments of Gulf War I. With just a few more explosions and special effects.

They're naturally disappointed. Some of the original production team may have dropped out, but we still had the film world's two most charismatic directors, both talking up the film. The screenplay had already been written. OK, the fighting was going to be a bit one-sided, but, hey, who's complaining? The film crew had been flown in from all around the globe. Now they're sitting around, bemused, playing cards, wondering what to do with all that expensive weaponry.

Thousands of extras - Kurds, mostly - had been written into the plot to add some local colour and push up the body count for CNN. It even seemed that the leading man was prepared to don that lovable walrus moustache one more time and reprise his most famous role as a crazed despot.

Gulf War II was planned as a made-for-TV pilot to introduce the viewing public to a more extended series in the pipeline, with a working title of World War III. It was 'all systems go'.

And then, at the very last minute, a stranger rides into Baghdad and hitches up his horse. He's quiet, softly spoken, almost diffident; he doesn't even carry a gun. It's a role that Jimmy Stewart used to play to perfection. And now, before you can say 'collateral damage', the film's been cancelled.

But there's nothing wrong with the plot of Gulf War II. With a bit of luck we'll be able to reassemble the production team again in five years' time. There'll probably be some new faces in the cast, but as long as that jovial bloke with the big moustache is still around there'll always be a chance we can finally get this film rolling.

In contrast, Milltown folk are waking up on a blustery Good Friday morning to news that seems unimaginably good. We almost hold our breath; can the Irish really have come to an agreement... about *anything*?

The participants emerge from their internal exile. They're caffeinated beyond sleep after so many hours of talk, yet filled with a restrained euphoria. They hardly dare show their feelings in case the Irish agreement turns out to be a false alarm... a mirthless practical joke... just one more telephone message with a coded warning.

One by one the pundits are wheeled out. In much the same way that Jack Charlton used to pick the national football team, anyone who can boast a half-Irish great-grandmother is adding their two-penn'orth of knee-jerk opinion to the growing debate. Nevertheless, it's remarkable to watch a country growing up before your eyes, and its people given a chance to be better than they sometimes think they are. In fact, one of the few dissenting voices comes - sadly, yet predictably - from the Union of Balaclava Manufacturers. In a terse statement they bemoan the end of hostilities and the prospect of imminent job-losses.

For far, far too long the political hardliners across the Irish Sea have been regarded as a benchmark for stubbornness, fanning the flames of resentments that should have been allowed to cool centuries ago. The regulars at the Grievous Bodily Arms have long recognised these men of violence as fellow travellers on the broad highway of intolerance.

These career drinkers - Milltown's own paramilitary wing - have adopted many of their attitudes. They're happy to resort to violence as *first* resort, in order to claim what is theirs by right. If they could only remember what that was. They maintain the right to march - albeit unsteadily - through any area of Milltown they choose. That's usually after midnight, and merely to commemorate having had a skinful. They soon forget why they're marching and settle instead for urinating in the front yards of teetotallers, light sleepers and other undesirables.

Stop press: That Irish agenda, in full...

1 Chairman's statement.

2 Apologies. Just the one major absentee: the Reverend Ian Paisley, who left a message to the effect that if he was speaking to anyone (which he isn't), it would merely be to announce that he wouldn't be attending the talks, and that on no account should anyone mistake this statement for any kind of apology.

3 Motion: Should we stop killing each other, or what?

4 Show of hands.

5 Any other business.

6 Tea and biscuits.

Shady Deals

Despite Milltown's growing reputation ("Isn't that where all the hippies live?"), it's barely more than a village in size. Not big enough, thank goodness, to have caught the eye of the acquisitive fast-food chains. Our sources of on-the-hoof eating - the Wok of Ages, the Kebab Take-away and a shoal of fish & chip shops - still maintain a sturdy independence. Nowhere in Milltown will you be asked: "Is that with fries?" Nowhere in Milltown will you have to reply: "No, thank you. I'm in full control of my faculties. If I'd wanted some chips, I'd have asked for them. Now get me my burger, you brazen young hussy, and be quick about it".

So it's quite a surprise when a stretch limousine rolls into town, and some big guys in suits get out. A crowd soon builds up: a big black car is quite a draw for Milltown folk who assume that a camper van painted with day-glo flowers still represents the height of motoring chic. And, outside of the embalming profession, such formal attire is quite a novelty in Milltown, where a more casual dress-code prevails.

The men are from Burger Chef Inc. They've come to see if Milltown is ready for their unremarkable fast-food fare, advertised with the sort of huge budget that immediately brands the product as thoroughly second-rate. If the food was any good, they could rely more on word-of-mouth recommendation ("Hey, had a Burger Chef burger today." "Any good?" "You betcha..."). But it's crap, of course, so names and logos need to be implanted, with surgical precision - and hypnotic repetition - into our frontal lobes. It's a scary business. But what's scariest of all is that the unsmiling guys in the expensive suits actually seem to believe every word they say.

Our impressionable councillors are no match for the silver-tongued blandishments of a posse of marketing executives. A handful of unsubtle bribes (a free haircut here, a car-ride there, and a wad of Burger Chef 'two for the price of one' vouchers that expired last year) is all it takes to create a co-operative atmosphere in the planning department. It's depressing - for a dozen different reasons - to find that the price of

Councillor Prattle's vote is just a badge with his name on it. Here in Milltown we can't even accept backhanders with any aplomb.

The wheels that grind so slowly for anyone wanting to put up a satellite dish are now spinning merrily, as the planning department discreetly rubber-stamps the application to install a branch of Burger Chef just outside Milltown. The plan depicts a gaudily-painted fast-food emporium, decked out in the primary colours that, like the burgers themselves, are designed to appeal primarily to the palate and attention span of a particularly hyperactive six-year-old.

Burger Chef's paint-by-numbers approach excludes skill and discretion from the cooking process. Instead of chefs they can hire unskilled, low-wage operatives who, by reading simple instructions and checking the glossy pictures on the wall, seldom go far wrong. Since plates have been dispensed with, even the dimmest of school-leavers can be trained to heap chips on a plastic tray.

Here in Milltown we know little about the devious ways of big business. And any acquisitions executive worth his salt would regard the annexation of Milltown into his company's fast-food empire to be an easy morning's work. But the Burger Chef mafia have underestimated the dedication of our local activists.

Using a combination of tact, diplomacy and small-arms proficiency, these brave eco-warriors insist that a new burger bar would contribute further to to the rape of our precious countryside. When the company's lawyer retorts with counter accusations - that the countryside was "dressed provocatively" and "leading them on" - their plans collapse into farce. Instead of yet another fast-food emporium, the people of Milltown will have a wildlife park, where the wildebeest can roam across the uninterrupted tundra of our overheated imaginations.

A Second Opinion

Whenever an over-worked GP writes a perfunctory prescription for tranquillisers - instead of listening to what his patient has to say - he unwittingly creates a job opportunity. Whenever conventional medicine admits to being stymied by some new and malignant virus, the door marked 'Alternative Therapies' opens a little further ajar. Whenever a patient is offered a gloomy prognosis, he is susceptible to the soft, seductive siren voices of complementary medicine.

Alternative therapies seem to occupy the middle ground between established religion and medical orthodoxy. The Church lurches erratically between laughable anachronisms and unseemly haste in jumping on the latest barmy bandwagon. Where the Church used to provide unequivocal moral guidance ("Repent or be damned...") it now offers the merest slap on the wrist to those who transgress. We in Milltown wince at the pathetic attempts of the Vicar of Saint Diana's to be hip and trendy. Acknowledging "the sanctity of indiscriminate shagging" isn't giving much of a lead to impressionable youngsters. And downgrading the Ten Commandments to the status of mere Performance Charters is unlikely to bring the doubters flocking back to fill his empty pews.

There was a time (with Queen Victoria on the throne) when the vicar of Milltown could terrify his congregation with a few home truths from the pulpit - leaving women weeping, men ashen-faced, children traumatised and damp. It was a time when the Devil walked among us, and wasn't just your dad dressed up. Guilt, fear and sin have put 'bums on pews' for almost two thousand years... but they don't play so well to the Pepsi Generation.

When church leaders get together now - to swap fashion tips ("Mmmm, purple..."), mull over vital ecclesiastical questions ("Can we still find a place in the Church for blind prejudice?") and generally try to put the 'fun' back into fundamentalism - the rest of us just stifle a yawn. And with the doctors offering unpalatable observations ("It's not good

22

for you, you know, all that crack cocaine on an empty stomach"), there are plenty of people in Milltown who'll pay good money to hear reassuring platitudes from a smiling therapist.

The therapists of Milltown are anything but cynical. They mean every word they say, which is worrying and comforting in about equal measure. It's a comfort to take your troubles, your stiff neck and your unregressed past lives to someone who will reinforce everything you say with empathy and understanding. But it's a worry that the people listening so intently to your litany of woes should themselves have only the most tenuous of toe-holds on reality.

Here in Milltown we're a bit top-heavy with people who promise, perhaps rather glibly, to heal your life. The newsagent's window is a patchwork of their tiny notices, each one showing just what professional results can be obtained with a John Bull printing set and an unfettered imagination. You only have to rub your neck wearily in Milltown to have half a dozen pastel-coloured business cards thrust into your hand.

One day an ambitious entrepreneur - some Bernard Matthews of self-basting therapies - may grab this whole unregulated business by the scruff of the neck and create some appalling multinational conglomerate. The MacDonalds of Meditation; the Toys 'R' Us of Transactional Analysis; the Coca Cola of Colonic Irrigation. Perhaps we could get all the masseurs under one roof, modelled on Nevada's infamous Chicken Ranch. With compliant girls to welcome the punters: "Hi, honey, wanna good time, huh? Wanna get *real* relaxed?" Or maybe not...

We can all re-invent ourselves as whatever we want to be. So Dope Dealer has remodelled himself as a Substance Abuse Negotiator, and the barmaid at the Grievous Bodily Arms now calls herself a Sex Therapist. Milltown's elder citizens have the opportunity to waste their old-age pensions on a few sessions of Empire Deprivation Treatment. Post-Keegan Trauma Counselling is available for distraught Newcastle fans. Even our Town Drunk, trying to get in on the act, is applying for a grant to teach self-empowerment through binge-drinking.

Having come to terms with her own deficiencies with mop, broom and duster, Willow Woman is offering sessions on Housework Neglect Assertiveness. She inspires other women to confront their own slovenly habits head-on, without embarrassment or self-consciousness. She encourages them to stop apologising, whenever a visitor calls, about their untidy homes. Instead of rushing around - plumping up cushions, tossing old magazines into the bin and kicking childrens' toys under the sofa - they are soon able to survey their unsanitary surroundings, look the visitor straight in the eye and say, without a hint of apology: "Yeah, it's a pigsty. Who gives a shit? Let's go out...".

A Watching Brief

Thanks to the efforts of Milltown's activists, an unremarkable area of scrubland just outside of town is still beyond the reach of the developers' grasp. The plans for a branch of Burger Chef have been shelved, hopefully for good. Locals had been surprised to learn just how many rare species of flora and fauna had made this scrubland their home. Once the battle had been won, however, sightings of endangered species declined to a more familiar rosta of sparrows, weeds and horseflies. The editor of the *Milltown Times* was almost persuaded by a misguided naturalist that the Thomson's Gazelle was now extinct in the South Pennines, and that its passing deserved to be mourned in newsprint.

The scrubland has been saved, but only at a price. So riddled was the land with the protesters' labyrinthine tunnels that torrential rain caused the land to subside. With a moistly flatulent noise - imagine a million cows lifting a leg simultaneously out of wet mud - the scrubland suddenly gave way. It was just good fortune that it happened in the night, otherwise there would have been many more casualties. As it was, an adulterous couple in a discreetly parked car were left with superficial bruising and a lot of explaining to do. Not least, how a company Mondeo with steamed-up windows came to be marooned on an island in the middle of a lake near Milltown.

The event was duly reported in the *Milltown Times*, though the editor decided to spare the couple's blushes. "There's no point in making enemies", he rationalised, as he put the finishing touches to that week's headline: 'Milltown Man Loses No-claims Bonus'.

The town has witnessed so many changes over the last few years that Milltown folk take the lake's overnight appearance in their stride. Now that spring is here, the water-margins are softened by reeds and bulrushes. Overhanging trees are blossoming with candy-floss colours. A pair of Mallard ducks have take up residence and, finding a safe haven on the back-seat of a rusting Ford Mondeo, are building a nest.

More by accident by design we finally have the nature reserve we were promised, where bird-watchers can scan the scene for unusual species. The developers had been thwarted by an imaginative list of unusual species that would have been lost to the bulldozers. So it's rather ironic that a blustery morning during the spring migration should bring not one but two rare birds to our little lake.

There's a Semi-Palmeated Sandpiper, standing exhausted and disoriented in the shallows, which should, by rights, have been in Southern Europe. There's a Wilson's Phalarope, looking lost and out of place among the more commonplace Coots and Moorhens, that the bird books suggest should be summering in California. And all around the lake is a rapidly-swelling gaggle of excitable twitchers, armed with high-powered telescopes... who really ought to be at work.

The English Marinade

It's the first day of the cricket season so, naturally enough, the weather is positively Arctic. The editor of the *Milltown Times* sits in his tiny office, staring distractedly through the window at the unseasonal flurries of snow. A troubled man, his gloomy mood is echoed by this unexpected resumption of winter. A letter lies face down on his cluttered desk.

His pre-lunch routine (coffee, crossword, cigarette, crap...) has been brought to well-honed perfection by years of journalistic indolence. But that routine has been rudely disrupted by the morning's post. There's a watery feeling in his bowels, and an unpleasantly light feeling in his head. Having read the letter once, he can hardly bring himself to look at it again.

A local newspaper is supposed to reflect the tenor of local life, but the *Milltown Times* has lost its way over the years. It's been allowed to drift in the doldrums of editorial neglect. On how many other newspapers, for example, would a story be summarily spiked for being 'too interesting'?

The editor has developed the unerring knack of elevating the dull and the trivial into headline stories, and burying anything of genuine significance towards the bottom of page five, next to the results of the Women's Institute's Most Exciting Tea-towel Competition. So resistant has he become to the siren voices of newsworthiness that he would no longer recognise a good story if it crept up behind him and bit him on the arse. He takes a long hard look at what makes Milltown shine in the presence of the town's less exalted neighbours... and then ignores it altogether.

The result is that Milltown - a town that fairly buzzes with creative endeavour, boasting a host of fascinating characters and a hard-earned reputation for eccentricity - is served by a newspaper for which even mediocrity would represent an unfeasible ambition.

For as long as he can remember, his journalistic life has meandered uneventfully through the tranquil backwaters of local affairs. If you discount the regulars at the Grievous Bodily Arms - generally a good idea, whatever the context - then the people he writes about every week are the very same people who read the paper. There isn't much call, in a small town, for scoops, exclusives and salacious headlines. A blistering exposé of nefarious goings-on might briefly attract a few extra readers. But what's the point, he reasons, of upsetting everybody just to double the sales figures?

With a sigh of resignation, the editor turns the letter over. It's from the managing director of the paper's publishing company who, a few years back, had won a job-lot of local newspapers in a crooked poker game. The company accountant, already late for a liquid lunch, had hidden away the first annual figures from Milltown in the petty cash column. That set an irreversible precedent; in order to balance the books in the years that followed, the *Milltown Times* was conveniently erased from company records. So it came as quite a surprise to the publishers to find that not only did Milltown have a newspaper of its own, but that they actually owned it.

Once they'd found Milltown on the map (a map so old that much of the South Pennines was uncharted territory and labelled, enigmatically, 'Here Be Dragons') a letter was hastily dispatched. Couched in polite yet unambiguous terms, it asked the editor to account for the paper's financial deficiencies over the years.

Our editor's careworn reverie is interrupted by his sub, who drops a fragrant, paper-wrapped parcel onto the desk. It's his lunch: fish, chips and scraps, as it is most days. What *is* the magic ingredient in newsprint that transforms a simple meal into something that smells so appetising? Newsprint, salt and vinegar: the English marinade.

The *Milltown Times* is celebrating its centenary this year. Launched during the last years of Queen Victoria's reign, the paper first found success as a cure for insomnia. Since then, of course, it has witnessed - and largely ignored - the most momentous events of the twentieth century. The editor had planned to bring out a special facsimile edition of that very first issue, but abandoned the idea when he realised it looked much the same as what he's publishing today. Even that very first headline had a familiar ring to it: "Mafeking Relieved: No Milltown Residents Involved."

It's easy to knock a local newspaper for being parochial and dull, but it's become part of our lives. A subscription to the *Milltown Times* makes an ideal present for an uncherished relative, or anyone who has left the area and might want to keep abreast of local issues. There'll be nothing in the paper to disturb delicate sensibilities and, indeed, nothing to make the recipients regret for an instant their decision to have left Milltown.

When the letter from his publisher is followed up by a phone-call - "Make a fucking decision for once in your life" - the editor is left open-mouthed with shock. However, we should never underestimate the obstinacy of weak men. His first idea for making the paper more profitable - selling it pre-shredded as hamster bedding - is greeted with a snort of derision by his sub-editor. His second idea is to cut down on expenses. So it's goodbye to company bicycle clips and tea-time treats funded from the petty cash tin. When this idea, too, is openly mocked, our editor take his publisher's words to heart... and sacks his sub.

It's not easy to replace the only member of staff who really knew what he was doing. And, although she's easier on the eye, the temp who arrives from the secretarial agency seems disturbingly inexperienced. "What's that ringing noise?", she asks brightly. "It's a phone", the editor replies, with a shake of the head and a world-weary sigh.

One Man Went to Mow

The farmers around Milltown share one notable ability (alright, two, if you count their adoption of baling twine as an indispensible fashion accessory). When spring comes they know exactly - to the hour - when the grass begins to green up. The only other person who looks at grass so intently is the captain of the Milltown XI. He's standing on the cricket square right now, gazing at this unremarkable patch of turf with a quaint and proprietorial pride.

Last September he'd been ready to throw in the towel, and pack up cricket altogether. It's hard work leading a team of losers. And he was fed up of being mercilessly lampooned by his work-shy team mates, who felt that if a puerile joke at his expense was worth telling once then it was worth repeating over the course of a whole afternoon.

He knows there are many other ways that a man can spend his weekends. But as soon as he remembers what they are - joining the queues at the supermarket check-out, putting up shelves and visiting the in-laws - he needs little persuading to search in the back of the wardrobe for his mildewed flannels. So he'll be marshalling his team through yet another relegation battle in the lower leagues. Spring is, after all, a time of optimism, before unrealistic hopes have been sacrificed at the altar of bitter experience.

As he tries to bring a reluctant motor-mower to life, he thinks about the game that has occupied his summer Sundays since he was in short trousers. Cricket, unlike just about everything else that life can offer, has never let him down. It has never ended a potentially rewarding relationship with a mendacious platitude like "It's not you, it's me... I just need more space". Cricket has never borrowed money off him and then neglected to pay it back. Cricket has never made silver-tongued promises to him that subsequently turned to ashes.

Once you start to think about the game (and it's designed to be slow and boring, for this very purpose) cricket offers some distinctly uncomfortable home truths. In the world beyond the boundary rope ('real life', as it's generally known) there are many flags of allegiance, many contradictory codes of conduct. Our captain finds everyday life anarchic and bewildering; the rules seem to change, at random, the moment he begins to understand them.

But *inside* that boundary there is just one quixotic code, to which both teams happily conform: cricket would be meaningless otherwise. Cricket is a Utopian vision, re-created every summer weekend throughout the land, on lush parkland, village greens and reclaimed swamps like Milltown's own little ground. The game offers a tantalising glimpse of what life could be like if human-kind were ever to get its act together.

It comes as quite a shock to our captain - a life-long Labour supporter - to realise that a team operates best when presided over by a benign dictator. Consensus politics don't work on the cricket field. You can't take a vote on who's going to field down at third man - at the boggy end, where the huge, malicious horseflies are. The players have to be *told*.

Cricket remains full of odd little civilities. On winning the toss you *invite* the other team to bat or field. You clap an opposing batsmen out to the wicket, and you clap him back to the pavilion again - merely hoping the two occasions are not too far apart. When a bowler hits a batsman on the head, it's considered sporting to feign concern for his welfare, before striding back way beyond his bowling mark and trying to bowl the same ball again. Only faster. It's hardly any wonder that the bowlers' habitual complaint is "Umpire, the batsman's gone out of shape."

After the game the players repair to the pub. After a few pints of cooking bitter they tend to forget just how soundly they've been beaten. The team's performance will, in beery retrospect, be awarded a heroic perspective that was entirely lacking on the field of play. Yes, the unwarranted optimism of third-rate cricketers has lessons for us all.

The captain is preparing the wicket on his own. His team-mates have conveniently forgotten to turn up, but they'll all be there for the game itself. He should be miffed... but he's not. When he's walking behind an elderly Acme mower, with the sun on his back and the sweet scent of new-mown grass in the air, the captain of the Milltown XI is convinced that he has the ropes of life firmly in his grasp. For a few intoxicating moments he is a truly happy man.

Low Life

Combine a morbid imagination, a flawed view of risk assessment and a paranoia fuelled by watching too many episodes of Crimewatch... and you've got an Identikit picture of Mr and Mrs Middle England at the fag-end of the millennium. They've been led to believe that violence is something that happens - routinely and randomly - on the streets of our cities. They lock their doors every night, switch on their burglar alarms and pull their duvets apprehensively up to their chins. Sleep doesn't come easily to the fearful. They hope they'll survive till morning without having their throats cut from ear to ear, but they expect the worst.

The mad axeman, lurking in the shadows for his unwary victims, is a familiar template for demonic violence. Gangs of kids, high on crack and beyond control, roam the mean streets of the nation's overactive imagination, prepared to bludgeon little old ladies to death to fund their spiralling drug habits. Men with khaki fatigues, unblinking eyes and a grudge against society are loading pump-action rifles, before heading off to rake a crowded shopping mall with bullets. Or so the sensation-seeking press would have us believe. These cultural stereotypes help to create a conveniently supine electorate, too frightened of spectres and bogey-men to start the revolution. While they're worried about having their purse nicked, they'll have neither the time nor the inclination to man the barricades.

An Englishman's home isn't so much a castle... as a prison. Mothers keep their children in; old folk are frightened to venture out at night. We've traded in our precious liberty for what we fondly imagine is the safety of our own homes.

The truth, alas, is that our homes are probably the most dangerous places we will ever visit. It's here, behind those locked doors, that we are most likely to encounter violence, perpetrated by the people we know best: the very people who have pledged to love and protect us. The locks that keep the burglars out also give protection and impunity to domestic tyrants, wife-beaters and child-abusers. The inescapable conclusion is that if you are walking late at night down a dark alley, and hear footsteps behind you... best hope it's a total stranger and not someone you know.

Milltown, thankfully, doesn't have a big problem with crime. With everybody knowing just about everybody else, most robberies culminate with a red-faced burglar returning a bin-bag of valuables with an embarrassed shrug of the shoulders and the offer of a conciliatory pint. OK, we have our fair share of roughnecks, shysters and ne'er-do-wells, but they mostly drink out of harm's way, at the Grievous Bodily Arms, where the people most at risk from their crazed outbursts are each other.

Instead of celebrity felons, with their mobile phones, business cards and web-sites, Milltown just has a handful of incompetent crooks. To talk of a 'criminal fraternity' makes it all sound rather cosy: a friendly freemasonry of light-fingered gentlemen, with members' ties and special handshakes. But it's not like that here. The regulars at the Grievous Bodily Arms have no need of funny handshakes; an arm twisted sharply up the back is all that's needed to engage the attention of a fellow drinker for a few eye-watering moments.

On most nights of the week they will be huddled around a corner table, planning some new scam. But, in truth, it's pretty tame stuff. Selling contraband snuff, forging library tickets, rustling geese and organising protection rackets ("That's a lovely front yard you've got there; I'm sure you'd like to keep it that way...") represents the height of their criminal ambitions.

On the Treadmill

Prince Charles has ascribed his level of fitness to "a thousand years of breeding". It's the sort of statement that asks more questions than it answers. OK, once they've had some discreet tuition 'below stairs', most of our royals can become quite adept at breeding, if little else. But is the physique and stamina of our future king really such a great example of what can be achieved by a millennium of royal eugenics?

Royal dynasties have passed many characteristics down through the generations. Centuries of in-breeding have perpetuated a wide selection of physical defects, such as the Hapsburg Lip and the Simpson Overbite. Mental equilibrium can't be taken for granted either. Consider poor, deluded Edward VIII. It's hard to imagine giving up your throne for Mrs Simpson. Most men would think twice before giving up a *bus-seat* for her. The *Mrs Simpson Book of Make-up Hints* would make a pretty slim volume (Step 1: buy a tub of white face paint. Step 2: slap it on). What *is* it about ugly women that sets royal pulses racing?

Perhaps Prince Charles is thinking of jumping on the fitness bandwagon (or, rather, being lifted onto it by obsequious man-servants) and making an exercise video. However, a lengthy breeding programme has many practical drawbacks as a fitness regime. The video's slogan - something like 'Feel younger, fitter and slimmer in just a thousand years... or your money back' - is unlikely to send many couch potatoes waddling down to the video store.

Milltown has its own fitness suite, where unfeasibly slim young things cavort to music, pose in leotards and fly to their personal fitness trainers if they put on as much as an ounce in weight. Access to this haven of narcissism is denied to the flabby and unfit - Town Drunk amply fits the bill - by the simple ruse of fitting a ferociously strong spring to the entrance door.

Exercise? Our Town Drunk finds it hard enough just to roll out of bed each afternoon. A sedentary lifestyle of daytime TV and binge drinking, lost in a masturbatory miasma, is wreaking predictable havoc on his metabolism. Though still young - technically - his beer belly, matching set of chins and ruddy 'Fray Bentos' features give him the unhealthy look of a professional darts player.

He's tried the traditional methods of looking slimmer - such as hanging around with fat people - but to no avail. Thanks to the deodorant he was given for Christmas, by the grateful manager of his local off-license, at least he doesn't have to smell of piss *all* the time. But in those occasional, scary moments of relative sobriety, he's depressingly aware that life is passing him by.

Indolence is almost an art-form here in Milltown. It drives Mr Smallholder wild to see so many people wandering aimlessly about, enjoying the spring sunshine. His diary is full: he's got places to see and people to do. *He* can't dress like a cockatoo. *He* hasn't got the time to stand on the old packhorse bridge and watch the world go by. *He* can't afford to sit around in the square, waiting for an experimental cocktail of recreational drugs to kick in. It drives him wild because he's stuck in a traffic jam. Workmen are erecting a palisade of cones around yet another hole they've dug in the road, before they knock off for a liquid lunch. The only thing that keeps an impatient financier sane at such moments of stress is repeating, through gritted teeth, a restorative mantra of FT100 share prices.

Owners of 4x4 vehicles can look down - literally - on other drivers, and enjoy the kudos of owning a vehicle with the aerodynamic qualities of a housebrick. So it's particularly galling to be stuck in a traffic queue, instead of being parked up on a mountain top. Having just forked out twenty-five grand to enjoy the car's renowned off-road capabilities, Mr Smallholder feels able to tackle the roughest and least hospitable terrain that the valley can offer - such as the speed-bumps in Tesco's car-park.

Those intimidating 'bull-bars' on the front aren't there just for show. OK, the chances of running into a bull - or being charged by a rhino - are pretty slim, even in Milltown. But pedestrians can get aggressive too. Especially if they've just been knocked over by a 4x4 driver who's preoccupied by making a call on his car-phone. And a little old lady, once roused to anger, can do a lot of damage to expensive paintwork with a shopping trolley and a bone-handled umbrella.

Dog Days

There are many kinds of silence. There's the embarrassed silence you get at breakfast in a seaside boarding house, which makes the tinkling of tea-cups seem deafening by comparison. There's the blissful silence when a migraine-inducing car alarm finally drains the battery and whines to a merciful stop. There's the brooding silence at the heart of a marriage when love has died. But best of all are those moments when the chatter of the mind abates, when memories, ambitions and everyday worries evaporate like puddles on a hot pavement, and - however briefly - you are blessed with stillness.

It's late spring, and the cherry blossom has blown away like wedding confetti. The world seems to have been washed clean by overnight rain; now the sun is shining out of a cloudless and untroubled sky. It's perfect. There are a few precious days every year when the leaves on the trees glow with an almost hypnotic shade of green, as though lit from within. When the swallows, swifts and martins race and scream above the town, seemingly for the sheer joy of scything effortlessly through the air. When the more irritating members of the insect world have yet to muster in numbers. When almost anything seems possible. And this - Cup Final day - is one of them.

There's no better time of the year to skive, loaf, dawdle, dally, hang loose, take things easy, stand and stare, shoot the breeze, twiddle our thumbs, kick our heels, and generally let the grass grow under our feet. Here in Milltown we have learned to enjoy the lexicon of leisure, and the warm weather is encouraging people to congregate in the little square in the middle of town.

There's an impromptu festival of belly buttons, as girls compete to see who can wear the skimpiest outfit. Girls with impossibly perfect breasts: the kind you could draw with a pair of compasses and two maraschino cherries. Girls for whom earth-motherhood is still years - and half a dozen dress sizes - away.

A solitary bongo player supplies the rhythmical soundtrack to a sunny afternoon of sloth and forgetfulness. A hippy girl sits cross-legged behind a small selection of hand-made jewellery displayed on black velvet. In the aftermath of the local elections, with time unexpectedly on his hands, Ex-Councillor Prattle is seeking solace in an alfresco pint. He wonders whether appropriating President Clinton's election slogan - "Kiss it, bitch" - was really such a wise decision. By the end of a lazy, languorous day, spring has slipped imperceptibly into summer.

We work when we have to, but there's no point in making extra work for ourselves, particularly on a sunny day. As Town Drunk says, with irreproachable logic: "Why take your clothes off when you go to bed? You're going to have to put them all on again in the morning".

Since there aren't enough jobs to go round, a lot of Milltown folk have selflessly passed up their own chance to embrace 9-5 drudgery, in order to let someone more deserving have a crack at it instead. Wounded Man had started work in the building trade, but had an enforced career change when he found he was allergic to Radio 1. Taking more readily to gardening, he found he had green fingers, but, hey, that's syphilis for you. The outdoor life suits him. It gives him a chance to day-dream, until something jolts him back to reality. Like inadvertently flaying a fresh pile of dog shit with a rebellious Strimmer.

We try not to become enslaved to the tyranny of the work ethic. After all, in these uncertain times, first prize in the lottery of life amounts to nothing more than the offer of another month's employment. Industrial relations have been reduced to a simple tactic: just keep the work-force paranoid and fretful.

We have to scratch our heads to recall the last time there was a strike in Milltown. It was, in fact, the Union of Corn Dolly Makers, who got a bit stroppy in the late seventies. Alas, the militant talk seemed disproportionately strident for such a small membership, and their rallying cry - "One out, both out" - signally failed to bring Milltown to its knees.

Niche Marketing

It's reassuring, in a cynical world, to find that Princess Diana's memory is being kept alive by a host of souvenirs, each one personally vetted for taste and decorum by an accountant with a pocket calculator. It's a job that certainly needs doing. After all, for every officially-sanctioned 'Di 'n' Dodi' fridge magnet or colonic irrigation kit, there's an awful lot of worthless tat flooding the market.

Those Princess Diana scratchcards, for example... though a spokesman remains unrepentant. "Look, I don't see what the fuss is about. All the money goes to charitable causes, such as funding the efforts of cash-strapped debutantes to follow Diana's sterling example and marry into royalty. The card features three little pictures of the Princess, which you scratch off. If you get three Dodi Al Fayeds you win the jackpot. Three James Hewitts will win £5,000. Even one Will Carling will net you a fiver. What's is so tasteless about *that*?"

Those Princess Diana dolls, though: tacky or what? "Not all at," he remonstrates, "it's not like they cry real tears or anything". On hearing this statement the Vicar of Milltown - a man who can recognise a heaven-sent publicity opportunity from a thousand paces - drops to his knees in wonderment.

Every Sunday he gazes down from the pulpit at his dwindling congregation; it's disheartening to realise that the only other time they muster in numbers is in the post office on pension day. The opportunity to celebrate the great days in the church calendar - Easter, Lammastide, the Third Sunday after Ascension - has failed to engage a generation raised on UFO encounters and the X-Files. And now, just as he's sinking in an ocean of apathy and unbelief, he's being thrown a welcome life-line.

"It's a miracle", he cries, arms raised aloft, his words echoing prophetically around the walls of his empty church, "truly a miracle...".

Within minutes, Milltown's bush telegraph being what it is, an excitable crowd has assembled at the Church of St Diana. The vicar looks on approvingly; the last time the church had been this full was when Linda Lovelace accepted an invitation to preach on 'Oral Sex: Its Place in the Sacrament'. "Form an orderly queue", our vicar entreats, vainly, as a tidal wave of unreconstructed credulity threatens to get out of hand. "Everyone will be able to see it, if you just..." The rest of his words are lost in the headlong rush to the altar rail.

Propped up in a recess occupied, until recently, by an obscure Old Testament prophet, is a Princess Diana doll. Due to a design flaw, with the arm being jointed only at the shoulder, she is either offering benediction to the assembled throng or giving a Nazi salute.

From all the various outfits supplied with the doll (*that* dress, landmine photo-opportunity khaki, suspiciously sweat-free gym leotard, Aids-victim consolation 'smart-but-casual', etc...) our vicar has plumped for the sort of undemonstrative dress the Princess used to wear when addressing one of her favoured charities about the issues that concern those working tirelessly in the voluntary sector. Such as bulimia, coping with a disfunctional family and the problems that stem from being married to a man who talks to trees.

As the people press forward to get a better view, they are struck dumb by the irrefutable evidence of what they can see. As they stare, open-mouthed, a solitary tear wells up from a kohl-rimmed eye, and rolls slowly down that pale porcelain face.

Travellers' Tales

If they have to make a choice between 'quality of life' and 'standard of living', there are many folk in Milltown who think: "no contest". When the highway of life is chock-full of frazzled motorists rushing headlong towards consumer heaven, we try to ensure that we are tootling along an empty carriageway in the opposite direction.

Milltown is a regular port of call, every summer, for a motley collection of clapped-out vans, for which MOT certificates and road-worthy tyres are but distant memories. The new-age travellers park up on a patch of waste ground just outside of town, between the river and canal: an area that attracts no attention whatsoever until a few crusties have the temerity to take up residence there.

The travellers come every year, but this year's a bit special. As part of Milltown's Midsummer Festival, they will be re-creating perhaps the most infamous event in their short history: the Battle of the Beanfield, when a bunch of travellers were given a severe pasting by over-zealous police. The travellers have even formed a troupe - the Frayed Knot - to research and perform this one-off event.

Authenticity is not a problem. It's easy, for example, to find original costumes: most of the travellers are still *wearing* them. The action, such as it is, mostly consists of running away and collapsing in agony beneath a hail of rubber truncheons: skills at which the travellers are already adept. And if an onlooker, concerned by these animated rehearsals, asks: "Are you alright?", a blood-stained traveller will be able to reply: "No, I'm a Frayed Knot".

Few aspects of life in Milltown polarise opinions so dramatically as the annual invasion of travellers. Dope Dealer thinks: "Customers". The police think: "Well-paid overtime". The old folk stuck in the Post Office queue behind a bunch of extras from the Mad Max movies think: "Bugger, it must be Giro day". Ex-Councillor Prattle thinks "Parasites" and, in demanding that the travellers be shunted across the county border, looks to win some easy plaudits from the beige-cardigan brigade. Professional Yorkshireman, writing his now blessedly infrequent columns in the *Milltown Times*, has some ready-made diatribes to offer, and so doesn't need to think at all.

New-age travellers make an easy target. And scapegoating one - preferably defenceless - sector of society is a ploy that's been used to devastating effect by tyrants and bullies down the ages. Even on the most pragmatic level, spending money from the public purse to shift a convoy of ramshackle vans out of Milltown is a 'solution' only to those with the most parochial of outlooks.

We have other visitors too, as the members of the Society for the Investigation of Unlikely Phenomena (Milltown Chapter) are only too keen to point out. The area around Milltown is known as UFO Alley, because of the large number of bizarre and unexplained sightings that have occurred here. What's really unexplained, however, is whether this signifies a genuine preponderance of UFOs, or merely reflects the number of people in town who, at any particular moment, are gazing vacantly skywards.

We've even had a close encounter of the *fourth* kind. Following a protracted lunchtime session, Town Drunk was abducted by aliens and, due to a mysterious depletion in the available gene-pool on distant planet Zob, forced to mate - repeatedly - with a beautiful, silver-skinned princess. He was deposited back on earth, unsteady but otherwise unhurt, a mere hundred yards from the Grievous Bodily Arms, but only after he'd been forced - at ray-gun-point - to hand over all the money from the pub's collecting bottle. Money that was to have funded the regulars' next outing. The landlord reacted remarkably well, considering. "These things happen", he acknowledged, while wondering how he would break the news to his regulars. They'd been looking forward to that seal-clubbing weekend for months.

All told, the abduction has done Town Drunk's reputation no harm. Instead of being thought of as just another guy who could use a shower, he's rumoured to have been offered signing-up fees by a couple of other pubs in town. He's happy, in truth, to reprise his story to anyone who realises just what thirsty work story-telling can be. And by the time he's repeated the tale a dozen times, it has assumed truly epic proportions.

He'd been too modest, at first telling, to mention that the denizens of a grateful planet had asked him - *begged* him - to stay on and assume the mantle of Supreme Time Lord of Zob. "I'd be a liar if I said I wasn't tempted", Town Drunk concedes, "but the beer was crap. Go on then, I'll have another pint. The strong one. Thanks".

Coming Home

Wow, what a summer of sport we have in prospect. We can anticipate a plethora of great sporting moments. Cricketers making off with a celebratory stump (yeah, what a fascinating collection *they're* going to make). Tennis players grunting like the soundtrack of a low-budget porno movie. Formula 1 drivers standing on the podium and drenching each other (*drink* that champagne, you over-paid tossers...). And when we get tired of sport altogether, there's always golf.

Soon we'll be pulling back the covers at Wimbledon; with its strawberries, cream and smug narcissism it's like the last outpost of Empire. No-one is allowed to forget, for an instant, that holding a grass-court tournament is something we do rather well. So expect the commentators to ask only leading questions: "What *is* it about Wimbledon, exactly, that makes it the most wonderful tennis tournament in the known universe, hmm?" And everyone, bless 'em, understands that the best thing is to humour our delusions. "Yes", they'll say, on cue, "there's nowhere quite like Wimbledon...", in a tone of voice usually directed at a small child seeking praise for a talentless finger-painting.

Then there's football. Love it or loathe it, there'll be no escaping it this summer. Even our Town Drunk, recently abducted for his notional reproductive prowess by the desperate denizens of planet Zob, is vaguely aware that the World Cup has finally arrived.

It's one thing to be there in person, enjoying the sights, sounds and smells of football in France: doing the hokey-cokey with fellow inebriates from around the globe. But here in Milltown we are adopting the more traditional approach: staying home, stocking up with microwave pizzas and a few crates of lager, pulling the living-room curtains tightly closed to keep the summer sunshine out, and enjoying blanket World Cup coverage on TV. The baffling Gallic symbolism of the opening ceremony... Hours of pointless pre-match predictions... Endless post-match analysis, proving merely that hindsight is indeed

20:20 vision... And, oh yes, a few undistinguished football matches squeezed in between...

Despite the much-publicised problems, the England players are beginning the campaign in good heart. Even Glen Hoddle's back-room staff will be having a friendly game: the psychics against the faith healers. The psychics have put both their footballing prowess and their professional abilities on the line by forecasting a five-nil win...

Football may be coming home, but only for a shit, a shave and a shower. Then it's straight off out again to paint the town red, have a skinful and give Johnny Foreigner a good seeing-too. Our hooligans will follow in the footsteps of their great-grandfathers, by laying waste to foreign lands in the name of Queen and Country. Without prejudice - happy to engage in hand-to-hand combat with people of every colour, race and creed. Taking to heart Churchill's famous exhortation, to "fight them on the beaches".

We won't win the World Cup, of course: failure is what we feel most comfortable with. And our sporting representatives aren't just crap at sport, they're crap at taking drugs too. Whenever you hear that some plucky British runner is "still in twelfth place, trying to get past the Lithuanian", you can bet your boots he'll test positive for drugs. It's humiliating. What's wrong with us? If we *are* taking drugs, then why aren't we taking them *properly*?

There's talk - maybe it's just idle chatter at this stage - about abandoning drugs-testing altogether. Let's face it: anyone who suggests that sport and drugs don't mix has never smoked a joint and watched synchronised swimming. Perhaps we could be more pragmatic and run 'drug-free' and 'drug-enabled' competitions side by side. At present we merely seem to be penalising those who manage their steroid intake badly, and rewarding those who do it well.

Flags of Convenience

W hat a puzzled and puzzling nation we are - beset with acute paranoia and a major identity crisis. One minute we're Great Britain: a small but pugnacious country, happy to roll up its sleeves at a moment's notice to sort out playground scraps around the globe and bang a few heads together. Then we're the British Isles: an off-shore atoll separated from mainland Europe by twenty miles of water and centuries of unwarranted bigotry. The next minute we're the United Kingdom: a threadbare, down-at-heel aristocrat, still insisting on respect from the riff-raff, even while the family silver is being discreetly auctioned off. To much of the world we're a bit of a joke.

Now - with the World Cup here - we are splitting, amoeba-like, into our constituent countries. We're even splitting up the flag. In the Union Jack we have a flag that only 1% of the population knows how to fly the right way up (with 99% not giving a toss either way). And the only people who drape themselves in it are drunken football fans and rabid members of the National Front. We raise the flag of St George when England are playing, of course, but what should we be singing? The National Anthem? Land of Hope and Glory? The Referee's a Wanker? The Scots, at least, are united in a song than sums up their own resentful aspirations: You're Not Getting The Oil Back.

You could drop these little islands into the middle of Lake Superior, and they would leave barely a ripple. We're not so 'Great' any more, and as for 'United', well, half of the population seems hell-bent on dividing our already fragmented nation into ever-smaller units. The Scots and the Welsh will get their parliaments. We might as well let the Welsh keep their language, on the basis that no-one else could possibly want it. As for Ireland: well, most of us would happily unhitch the mooring ropes and let it drift off towards the Faroe Islands.

The Isle of Man will continue to enjoy its special status as a haven for tax exiles and devotees of corporal punishment. The Socialist Republic of South Yorkshire wouldn't mind going it alone or, failing that, giving some toffeee-nosed twat a bloody nose just for the hell of it. The South of England will carry on much as before: keeping schtum and banking the money.

For those who live in Milltown it's always fun to have visitors from Down South, if only to confirm all their prejudices about Life Up North. We're supposed to be friendly and open. We don't lock our doors (which makes it a doddle to slip inside and knock off a video). Southerners suggest we are chauvinistic too, but, by gum, we've got an awful lot to be chauvinistic about. To anyone who accuses us of being straight talking... rude, even, we have a ready answer. We say: "If you don't like it up here, you bouffant-haired shirt-lifter, then fuck off back Down South"...

But we reserve the full force of our disdain for that most loathsome of creatures, the Professional Yorkshireman. A Yorkshire Quisling who's sold his self-respect for the Southerners' shilling, and who colludes in his transformation into a two-dimensional cartoon character. A dancing bear whose crude steps offer a basic kind of amusement. A novelty act. A skateboarding duck.

It's depressingly easy to play the Yorkshire card. You start with 'gruff, unbending intransigence' and 'mule-like stubbornness'... and just go downhill from there. Producers of current affairs programmes like to keep a few Professional Yorkshiremen on hand, in case an otherwise uninspiring debate needs stirring up by a loud-mouthed buffoon who loves nothing better than the sound of his own voice. It's a simple device, aimed at making the other pundits look reasonable and rational by comparison. Professional Yorkshiremen are wheeled in whenever a discussion threatens to subside towards affability and concord. They represent Yorkshire... but only in the way that a session at the Grievous Bodily Arms represents a good night out.

News from the Front

As we race into the final bend of the last lap of the twentieth century, it's men who seem to be moaning loudest about their lot. All those magazine articles - What Are Men *For?* - are taking their toll on our self-esteem. They're infiltrating those areas of the male psyche where more traditional interests - football, beer and sex - ought to be.

Men's customary place at the head of the nuclear family seems to have been usurped. And the nuclear family itself seems to be going the way of nuclear weapons and nuclear power: recognised as just another failed experiment in domination. If men are surplus to requirements - no longer needed to carve the Sunday joint, put up shelves or be a convenient bogey man to frighten naughty children ("Just wait till your father gets home...") - then what *does* the future hold for us?

In the past we've tended to regard self-analysis - along with weeping uncontrollably - as activities best left to women. They do it so much better. And for so much longer. Whenever men *do* unlock their emotions, it's a shame that the emotions they tend to express most often are either blind rage or maudlin self-pity. So we're trying to get in touch, instead, with our more nurturing side. We read copies of *Cosmopolitan* - openly, brazenly - and not just the bra ads either. But whenever we collapse in floods of tears - perhaps our football team has lost - we're given no credit whatsoever.

In the age-old war between the sexes, Wounded Man is one foot-soldier who has arguably spent too much time behind enemy lines. He listens - a lot - to women's problems and concerns. On Mondays, Wednesdays and Fridays he can usually be found sitting at a stripped pine kitchen table, in one terraced house or another. He'll be cradling a mug of herbal tea, gnawing at a home-made biscuit and nodding understandingly while a woman with wild eyes and unruly hair is emoting at interminable length.

He's done his best, God knows, to be what the women he knows say they want men to be. He's tried to tap into his feminine side (he's not gay, exactly... he'd just be prepared to pitch in if they were short-handed). He's come to see women not merely as sex objects but as co-travellers down the rocky road of life. He resists making chauvinistic assumptions about a woman's sexual proclivities. In short, he's become so benign and docile that the women of Milltown have come to see him as just part of the furniture. They don't consider him as a sexual being any more, just a willing ear. Which means that all he ever gets is *aural* sex. It's so long since he last had a tumble under the duvet that he can't even remember who gets tied up first. The most exciting thing that happens to him in bed these days is cramp. In the gender war he's no longer even mentioned in dispatches.

The final humiliation came when Wounded Man was beaten up by a twelve-year old. He tried to rationalise the situation: *he* was taken by surprise... *she* was big for her age. But there's no escaping the fact that his pride - as well as his face - has taken a battering. When Willow Woman called round, to announce that her inner child was starting nursery, she was too self-absorbed to offer much sympathy. "Take it like a man", she had said, unthinkingly, before leaving him alone to cry hot tears of humiliation.

The truth hurts. Not as much as having your testicles wired up to a car battery, of course, but that's scant consolation to a man in pain. Wounded Man knows he's got to find a way to rediscover his manhood. It's been swamped by a tidal wave of uncritical empathy and emotional honesty: it's what can happen when you spend too much time in the company of women.

A man needs to stand on his own two feet, look the world straight in the eye and say "This is what I am. There's nothing to apologise for. OK, I'll take a shower..." in an unequivocal statement about his own masculinity. He needs to run with the wolves, shit in the woods and enjoy relationships with other men that can include farting contests.... but isn't merely defined by them.

So it seems like providence is taking a hand when Wounded Man spies an unassuming little poster in the newsagent's window, advertising the first ever meeting of the Milltown Men's Group.

Wise Women

When Willow Willow switches on her radio to enjoy some soothing music - it's Dolphin Hour on Crystal FM (or maybe it's Crystal Hour on Dolphin FM) - she finds it's tuned to the news instead. She listens for a minute, with her hand on the dial, idly reflecting when she'd last heard the words 'oral sex' and 'Oval Office' in the same sentence. She's startled to hear that, according to a recent poll, ninety per cent of American women have said they wouldn't dream of giving Bill Clinton a blowjob... ever again. What's going on, she wonders?

It always comes as quite a surprise to Willow Woman to realise that there is more happening in the world than exists inside her own head. With a wave of her hand - a delightfully soft hand, a hand unchapped by housework - she can brush away the world and its worries like a tiresome fly. It's easy... well, it's easy if you're Willow Woman and you're more than usually self-engrossed. She's getting a little tense in the run-up to the millennium: with Venus in the ascendant, and Phallus rising, she's got a lot on her mind.

She's not alone; Milltown is chock full of Wise Women who claim special insights, based on the interpretation of signs, portents and premonitions. Of genuine powers there appears to be more hint than evidence: just a meaningful tap on the nose here, a knowing smile there. Yet it would take someone bolder than Wounded Man to suggest that these powers of clairvoyance might be subjected to a little objective scrutiny. Predicting the winner of the 2.30 at Kempton would make a convincing start.

You can press Willow Woman on the matter and wonder what she *can* foresee, and she'll say, with that little smile and one raised eyebrow: "Well, I knew you were going to say *that*". You could rise to the bait, but what would be the point? If you wanted a life filled with logic and rationality, then why the hell did you move to Milltown in the first place? The Wise Women of Milltown occupy a land beyond parody: a place where words can mean exactly what they want them to mean. It's beguiling, in that Alice in Wonderland kind of way, to put common sense to one side for a while and lose yourself in their impenetrable psychobabble. You won't be short of company.

Willow Woman's faith in intangible forces extends to her car: one of those 'half-timbered' Morris Travellers that looks like Anne Hathaway's Cottage on wheels. It's knackered, basically. When the second-hand car salesman saw her coming, he rubbed his hand together; he knew his monthly sales bonus was in the bag. He, too, has special insights: he can spot a soft touch a mile away. Willow Woman's body language - her aura, if you will - seemed to be suggesting: "I've had my frontal lobes removed and I've got a Barclaycard".

She doesn't know why her car goes, and she doesn't know why it stops. It seems to run on the motive power of pleas and prayers. Instead of filling up with petrol she tries, through the power of psychokinesis alone, to persuade the needle on the petrol gauge to creep out of the red. It means she misses a lot of appointments, sometimes by a matter of days.

A lot of people in Milltown share Willow Woman's ambivalent attitude to cars. We don't really approve of them: if more people could be persuaded to give up their noisy, smelly, environmentally unsound vehicles... then there'd be more room on the roads for *us*.

To emphasise our distaste for the internal combustion engine, we take a perverse pride in knowing as little as possible about what goes on under the bonnet. We're happy to give our cars affectionately silly names, but that's about the limit of our involvement. The result, predictably, is that the local garage, Lesbian Motors of Milltown, has a regular throughput of old bangers - cherished, but determinedly unmaintained - to sort out.

When our clapped-out cars quietly expire at the side of the road, due to lack of petrol, oil or water, we are mystified. We spring immediately into action, open up the car bonnet and give the engine a long hard stare. We try to shame it back to life. We're prepared to get our hands dirty, but if cleaning out the ash-trays *doesn't* bring a recalcitrant engine spluttering back into life, what then? It's at times like this that we wish we could number more car mechanics in our circle of friends, and fewer performance poets.

Mr Smallholder, conversely, prefers to own a car that reflects his position and social aspirations. For a man of means it's an easier option than going to the trouble of developing something more useful... like a personality. He'll rhapsodise about the gearbox of his latest motor ("It's *sooo* smooth... like pulling a greasy stick out of a dog's bottom") or the indisputable pleasure of sending small mammals to meet their maker with just a light, last-minute touch on the power steering.

His main criterion, when considering a new car, is whether the lower orders could afford one. "After all", says Mr Smallholder, feeling he's on safe ground, "it's not as if the poor breathe the same air as we do, is it?" "Actually", suggests the salesman in the showroom, "I think you'll find that they do". "But that's just a figure of speech, a metaphor". "No, I promise you, sir: the poor really *do* breathe exactly the same air as as we do". "Well, I'll be damned...", says Mr Smallholder, with purse-lipped annoyance, while making a mental note to buy his next car elsewhere.

Festivities

It's been one of the wettest Junes in living memory. The local GPs are steeling themselves for the inevitable influx of patients - mostly young, some old enough to know better - suffering from Glastonbury Trenchfoot.

Milltown has its own Midsummer Festival. We followed the usual custom by engaging a second-rate celebrity to open the event. If this was any other festival our choice of luminary might have seemed wilfully provocative. But this is Milltown, and we were convinced that a famous drug-smuggler (star of stage, screen and Crimewatch: known as the man who put the 'smug' into 'smuggling') would give the festival a modicum of street credibility.

We were led to believe he was a reformed character, enjoying a second - and equally lucrative - career as an author, speaker and stalwart of the chat-show circuit. But, sadly, he reverted to type on arrival in Milltown: ignoring the ribbon and cutting a line of coke instead. When he made an unconvincing appeal to the young folk of Milltown - "Hey kids, take my advice and avoid people who take drugs... like the narcotics squad" - he was promptly drummed out of town.

With that unhappy event behind us, the festival is now in full swing. Milltown's cinema has re-opened, following a refit, with a special showing of *Titanic*. The manager was gratified to see how many of the audience had come, as requested, dressed as Titanic survivors. He wasn't to know they'd just been caught in a sudden shower.

This year we have a variety of street entertainers: amusing enough, no doubt, to those whose idea of entertainment is digging a shallow grave. A clown is performing in the town square: gurning wildly, doing pratfalls, waving a bladder on a stick and frightening small children. We live in hope that someone will come along, do the decent thing, and quietly kick him to death. A mime artist, too, fails to stir the blood, with his attempts to walk into a strong wind, and escape from an imaginary room. The only thing we'd like to see him mime his way out of is a lead-lined-coffin. Get out of *that*, you whey-faced buffoon...

An evening of 'Songs From the Shows' will celebrate the derivative work of Sir Andrew Lloyd-Webber, who bestrides the world of popular music like a colostomy. More sober-sided Milltown folk anticipate the first performance of a brand new symphony - *Pretentious Title Number Three* - written for cordless drill and car alarm. It promises to be a challenging work: simple yet complex; forthright yet ambiguous; under-stated yet monumental; immensely significant and yet, at one and the same time, total and unmitigated bollocks.

The pubs of Milltown have suspended their usual moratorium on poetry for the duration of the festival. Except the Grievous Bodily Arms, of course, where a man with a silk cravat, a strange nasal whine and a slim volume of verse would be happy just to get out alive. The pub regulars have a chivalrous code of conduct that precludes them from hitting a man with glasses. But there's really no need, since the butt-end of a pool cue does the job far more effectively.

There's an unwritten rule amongst the drinkers of Milltown: you drink in one unexceptional pub or another, and then sneer at all the other pubs in town. It's like football. You support a team through good times and bad. It's *your* team, for no better reason than your dad took you to a game at the age of seven. You'll hear nothing bad about your team; you wish only ill to other teams. And it's *your* local: it's good because *you* drink there. OK, it's a rather simplistic notion. Then again, getting away from complicated, demanding concepts like relationships, car maintenance and double-entry book-keeping is precisely why we go to pubs in the first place.

There's a pub just outside of Milltown that has missed out on such misplaced loyalty. It's had too many facelifts, too many makeovers; no wonder the locals give the the place a wide berth. It's been an American diner, a tapas bar and - the strangest idea of all - a 'fun pub'. ("Fun?...", snorts the landlord of the Grievous Bodily Arms, "...don't make me laugh..."). Our more impressionable young folk used to stand at the bar - looking as cool as the ravages of acne would allow - swigging self-consciously from a bottle of over-priced foreign beer, the neck conveniently plugged with a segment of citrus fruit.

The pub's last incarnation but one was as the Jolly Roger: stuffed to the gunnels with shipboarding junk. Unfortunately, the manager took the pirate theme rather too literally and absconded with both the barmaid and a fortnight's takings.

Since then the pub has gone Irish. It takes a lot of money to recreate the distressed look of a genuine Irish pub, which is what it claims to be. Despite the expensive renovations, the only authentic touch has been to replace all the decent beers with cold, creamy tasteless crap. The inescapable conclusion, for those who have visited the place, is that genuine Irish pubs are in *Ireland*...

Having spent so much money on the pub, the brewery were forced to economise when it came to hiring staff. It's entertaining - in a grim, voyeuristic kind of way - to watch an ill-matched band of incompetents and malcontents bring the noble art of catering down to the level of a playground squabble.

A food order *should* initiate a seamlessly orchestrated series of events, culminating with a rosy-cheeked waitress sliding a steaming plateful under your nose. At Sheamus O'Tooles, however, a food order sets off a series of unconnected events which culminate in blind panic. The kitchen staff give convincing impressions of people who have never prepared a meal before. Every lunchtime seems to end the same way: with sounds of crockery smashing against the wall, screams of recrimination, the slamming of doors, the wail of a fire engine's siren, and the cook - an unshaven man with a grubby vest and singed eyebrows - sitting at the bar cradling a double whisky, trying to stop his hands shaking.

We wonder what the pub is going to turn into next, but we're not optimistic...

Second Thoughts

You need to be a farmer - or a certified insomniac - even to think of watching early-morning television. The farming programmes used to present the livestock prices. But now, with the future of hill-farming looking so bleak, auction prices just make farmers depressed. Instead, in an effort to send agricultural folk off to work with a light step and a song in their heart, the farming programmes are now relentlessly upbeat.

What nobody could have anticipated, though, was the instant appeal of *You've Been Farmed*: a cheap and cheerful montage of camcorder clips, based on Jeremy Beadle's ground-breaking show. Red-faced farmers are laughing themselves silly at these amusing and possibly unrehearsed vignettes of country life: accidents with hay balers, children falling into middens, and cross-species sexual encounters hilariously interrupted by a disgruntled farmhand with a hand-held video.

The jokes are lost on the beleaguered Smallholder family, for whom the fabric of rural life is unravelling fast. They're appalled by their farming neighbours: an antipathy that appears to be mutual. When they first arrived they had been gratified to find, on more than one occasion, that some local worthy had left a brace of pheasants in the Smallholders' porch. But those days are gone. If their farming neighbours leave anything now, it's more likely to be the steaming contents of a fully-laden slurry tank decanted provocatively in front of their double garage.

Back to the Bridge

Aspects of country life that initially seemed quaint and endearing now merely irritate. For one thing it's so bloody *noisy*. Farmers don't talk to each other; they *shout*. Their dogs bark all night. Even the monotonous bleating of grazing sheep tends to exacerbate Mrs Smallholder's migraines.

The countryside doesn't, after all, smell of fabric softener - especially when the wind is from the south. Mr Smallholder realises, too late, why their farmhouse had remained empty for so long before they moved in. When he asks his immediate neighbour whether it is really necessary to have so many dead animals around the place, the answer is hardly reassuring. The farmer shrugs his shoulders, noncommittally: "Nahhh", he says, "it's just a perk for the men".

Mr Smallholder is confused by the dumb insolence of his neighbours. He'd been looking forward to having a few picturesque yokels around the place, to add a sense of scale and a little local colour to the rural scene. But they don't even doff their caps to him, or, if they do, it's merely to wave them in a sarcastic parody of deference. They don't know how to behave. Instead of doing unspeakable things to semi-domesticated animals, they should be leaning on gates, chewing straw and misdirecting lost motorists. For a man who spends his working hours surrounded by toadies, lackeys and lickspittles, it's discouraging for Mr Smallholder to return home each night to nothing but scorn, slurry and sedition.

After a few months of attempted integration the Smallholders are spending more and more of their leisure hours with other disheartened exiles from the city. Liquor-fuelled evenings when they can let down their defences and admit that the much-vaunted attractions of country life are just lies and innuendo, shamelessly propagated by estate agents and the editors of glossy lifestyle magazines. Amongst friends they mutter conspiratorially about terse, unfriendly farmers who seem to appear - at any moment, without warning, their clothes in disarray - from sheep-fold and byre.

Talk usually turns to the attractions of the city: the very same lifestyle the Smallholders were so keen to abandon just a few months before. Shallow, meaningless relationships with other over-paid financiers never looked as good as they do now.

One Monday afternoon, already late for a meeting, Mr Smallholder is hurtling through Milltown in his Range Rover. Momentarily distracted by taking a call on his car-phone, he manages to miss a jay-walking freemason by inches... but only by mounting the pavement and wiping out a bus-queue of pensioners. As he prises the last shopping bag out of the bull-bars, he suddenly sees the folly of his ways. There's no time to waste: he storms into the estate agent's office. "You know that farmhouse you sold me six months ago?..." The lady behind the counter nods, apprehensively. "...Well, put the bloody thing up for sale again. And phone for an ambulance; I'm late enough as it is...".

Pioneers

The fortnightly meetings of the Milltown Antiquarian and Local History Society are held in a dusty room at the back of the library. The key is only available to members of the society and other registered pedants. Here, displayed in glass cases, are some of the archaeological finds made by the men whose fading photographs line the walls. Local history was a serious business late last century, to judge from their bleak, unsmiling features. With their full beards and piercing eyes, they display the passion of religious zealots. They could have been Old Testament prophets, or ministers of the cloth. Instead, they were intractable men of impeccable character, with rather more time on their hands than was good for them.

Two portraits stand out. The protagonists face each other across the room, and across the twentieth century; the steeliness of their gaze is undiminished. Both were well known in Milltown for their encyclopaedic knowledge of the town's history. Both published scholarly papers on their archaeological discoveries. Other historians held them in equal respect, even awe. But their heroic deeds in the amphitheatre of local history had a doomed, Shakespearian quality. Milltown was just too small a town to accommodate two great minds and, more to the point, two such monstrous egos.

When these two locked horns in a debate, the other society

members might just as well have crept out to enjoy a beer or two at the Poultry Dealers Arms. Which they often did. Whenever these two disagreed (and no matter was ever deemed too trivial to fuel a heated argument) you could be sure it was personal. Tightly-clenched fists would pummel leather-bound tomes, raising clouds of dust. And the more they disagreed, the more poisonously polite they would become.

Displaying the erudite skills and barbed observations of a pair of sparring lawyers, they fought long and hard over the custody of Milltown's heritage. They talked about each other in the third person, as though to distance themselves even further from views they found so repellent.

"I would like my learned friend to consider whether it might, in fact, be a more likely scenario that..."...

"Far be it for me, a humble seeker after truth, to question my colleague's grasp of a difficult subject. Nevertheless I would like to point out that..."...

It's no wonder that the local historians of the 1990s, busy delving into those same dusty tomes, can still feel the gimlet eyes of their antecedents boring into the backs of their heads.

The great days of the Milltown Antiquarian and Local History Society came late last century, when the textile industries were booming. The looms clattered and the mill-chimneys issued yellow smoke that hung in the valley and blackened the buildings. The future looked bright, at least for those who *owned* the mills. They weren't to know then what would happen to Milltown and all the other textile towns of Yorkshire and Lancashire. It's reassuring, in fact, to find that Milltown has any history at all, for this is a little town that almost died, before rising again like a phoenix from the flames.

During the 1950s and 1960s Milltown was in steep decline, with textile mills closing at a startling rate. The flames weren't merely metaphorical, with mill-fires being a more common occurrence than chance alone would suggest. It was like the Klondyke in reverse: people rushing to leave the valley in search of work. House prices slumped to the point where many people simply locked up their terraced homes and abandoned them.

Milltown was just one more town that had become over-reliant on a single, failing industry. Except that Milltown *didn't* die; it changed.

When a motley collection of utopian idealists were looking for somewhere to put down roots, they found that Milltown answered many of their needs. The town offered a reluctant embrace, throughout the 1970s, to the first wave of hippy settlers. It was a place where penury, eccentricity and unusual belief systems could co-exist with more orthodox outlooks. The settlers bought - for small change - terraced houses that might otherwise have fallen to the bulldozers, thus revealing rather more financial nous than their unconventional dress-sense might indicate.

The yuppies used to brag, during their interminable dinner parties, about how much their houses had risen in value between the starter and the sweet course. Now, a decade later, the hippies boast how *little* their houses had cost when they first arrived in Milltown. It's a strange inversion.

These early settlers retain a special place in our affections; they're our nobility. And the first family - our Kennedys, if you will - are the earliest hippy settlers of all: Arthur and Martha Fustian. They look like everybody's grandparents and - given the informal sexual attitudes that prevailed during the early 1970s - who's to say they aren't?

High Horse

We hear that Pakistan has joined India as elite members of the Nuclear Club. It's a headache for the West: what do these developing countries need nuclear weapons for? They're just not accustomed to handling deadly warheads. They might start pointing them at each other, just for a laugh, and set one off accidentally. Nuclear weapons? Best leave them to the big boys, eh, lads? People who know how to take the prospect of global meltdown in their stride.

Some folk can't sleep at night for worry. Green Man, for one: tireless keeper of the ecological flame here in Milltown. Having taken the troubles of the world onto his shoulders, he hasn't much time for levity. His confident assertion - "I have as good a sense of humour as the next man" - reveals either a man blessed with no sense of humour whatsoever, or a man standing uncomfortably close to Ian Paisley.

There's no doubt about it: our poor, battered, beleaguered world needs all the help it can get. If God really *has* given us custody of the planet, then we should be expecting a knock on the door any day now from a team of celestial social workers. Our lame and shame-faced excuses - "I don't know, maybe the earth slipped and fell, these things happen..." - will fool nobody. Look after the planet? Most of us find it hard enough to look after a *goldfish*...

Those who wantonly despoil the planet deserve all our anger and disdain. So we really should be giving Green Man a fraternal pat on the back for being so concerned, so single-minded and so incontrovertibly *right*. There's a fine line, however, between doing the right thing and being a complete pain in the neck, and it's a line he oversteps rather too often.

He like to thinks of himself as caring and open-minded. But political allegiance is circular, and those who embrace the far left and far right occupy more common ground than they would care to admit. In the great census of life they do seem to be ticking a lot of the same boxes. Though the Grievous Bodily Arms is the sort of pub that makes him shudder with distaste, Green Man's entrenched attitudes and hectoring voice would not seem out of place in Milltown's own den of vice. The pub regulars, quick to acknowledge bloody-mindedness when they see it, would immediately recognise him as one of their own, and move aside, with grudging respect, to give him standing room at the bar.

You can't knock Green Man's ideals; it's just a shame he has the demeanour of a pub bore. He feels obliged to bang on interminably about whatever is bothering him this week, taking as the text of his sermonising the well-know aphorism: 'Think globally, act pompously'.

Old habits die hard. Green Man steadfastly refuses to buy South African grapes, for example. It's not a hard decision to make: there's still that awful South African accent, loaded with years of unmerited privilege and, in any case, he's not keen on grapes. He won't buy products from countries with repressive regimes and poor records on human rights. So it's just an unfortunate accident of birth that he lives in Britain: a country which long ago took a swarm of rampaging locusts as a convenient template when framing its foreign policy. Green Man won't buy washing-up liquids that contain detergents or, indeed, any other ingredients that actually get the pots clean. It's not a problem for him, since his punishing schedule precludes anything as mundane as washing up.

You wish he'd relax now and again, and maybe let someone else have a turn at carrying the planet. But there's no room for complacency, he insists, while we face the threat of global warming. They say that towns such as Peterborough and Grantham could be lost beneath the flood-water, and that Milltown could become a coastal resort blessed with a Meditteranean-type climate, where trees laden with citrus fruit would add welcome splashes of colour to the gaunt gritstone landscape. Problem? *What* problem?

Green Man issues long-winded, ten-page press releases about the depletion of our deciduous woodlands. He's prepared to turn out, at a moment's notice, to campaign on the pressing issues of the day, but is always too busy to apply that second coat of Artex in the sitting room. He'll offer his free-range opinions on everything from acid rain to the closing of Milltown's public toilets. His convictions, at least, seem infinitely sustainable.

The Wherewithal

Wounded Man wishes he'd spent the last pound in his pocket on a lottery ticket, instead of another packet of joss sticks. He's convinced himself that the numbers on the last draw were just the kind of numbers he probably would have picked. But he's too late for this week's draw; he'll have to settle instead for the comforting smell of jasmine and patchouli to mask the more familiar stench of financial incompetence.

He slips his card into the cash machine - more in hope than expectation - and taps out his pin number. He finds that the usual message on the screen ('You're joking, of course') has been replaced by an altogether more cheerful proposition: 'Would you like cash?'. Wounded

Man is gobsmacked; it is a moment of almost religious clarity.

Money puzzles him. He doesn't have a clue about PEPs and TESSAs, and a 'basket of currencies' is something he can only guess at. He's totally foxed by stags, bulls and bears: the menagerie of the stock market. He's virtually innumerate, and working through a set of figures is a concept as alien to him as rotating the tyres on his ageing Vauxhall Ashtray. Whenever he glances at his bank statements, the numbers wander erratically across the paper like foraging ants. A man could have made a tidy fortune simply by looking at all the financial decisions Wounded Man has made over the last twenty years... and doing precisely the opposite.

Money has its own momentum, its own byzantine logic, its own arcane language. It's just not a language that Wounded Man speaks. So it's probably for the best that he wound up here in Milltown, where a proficiency with figures is not seen as a pre-requisite for a long and happy life. Where a man in a good suit braying "Buy pork belly futures... sell my grandmother" into his mobile phone can still turn heads and stomachs.

We're all expected to know about complex financial issues, but how do we actually find out? Most school-leavers can name the principle exports of Ecuador and all six wives of Henry VIII... but have never been taught how to balance a cheque account. Wouldn't it be useful, for example, to have a little caveat printed on the cover of every chequebook: *Just to let you know that you are dealing with a bunch of unprincipled bastards. Have a nice day.* Or on your mortgage documents: *Your house, your reputation and everything you hold most dear will be at immediate risk if you so much as* think *about missing a payment...*

Conversely, the simplest aspects of life often seem to be spelt out in superfluous detail. Like the instructions on the back of a shampoo bottle... as though anyone old enough to go shopping would actually be washing their hair for the very first time. And, amongst the bewildering variety of shampoos available, why do you never see one that's 'especially formulated for *dirty* hair'?

Or a packet of breakfast cereal: you'll get lists of every mineral, vitamin and trace element... per flake, per bowlful, and per hundred-weight. What you *won't* see is: *Ingredients: crap, mostly. OK, you* can get one twentieth of your daily vitamin requirements. *Big deal, you could get much the same nutritional value from nibbling the contents of a full Hoover bag.* And what about that serving suggestion: *Try a bowlful with cold milk?* What else would you do with corn flakes? Throw them on the floor? Pour them into your hat?

When it comes to product labelling, there are things you really need to know... and things you frankly don't. A toilet roll, for example, gives you the size of every sheet, the number of sheets per roll and the total length if, like one of those lovable Labrador puppies, you were bored enough to unravel it. Instead of more pertinent information, such as: *Have you ever wondered why these toilet rolls are so cheap? It's because they're made out of low-grade sandpaper and there are no perforations. Sorry...*

Then there are all those products which have consumer helplines. What bizarre set of circumstances is going to make a customer ring the number printed on, say, a bottle of mineral water? Unless it's to ask: "Can you help me? I've just spent good money on a bottle of water that costs about ten thousand times as much as the stuff that comes out of the tap. Could you recommend a good psychiatrist?"

There's even a phone number printed on cans of Special Brew. What kind of job is that, fielding calls in eight-hour shifts from the people who drink this stuff on a daily basis? "So you've just drunk five cans of Special Brew, and your legs don't seem to work? Well, thank you for calling"...

Piercing Cries

It's midsummer so there are plenty of visitors mooching around Milltown, looking for something to spend their money on. And our local shopkeepers are doing their very best to ensure that some of it comes their way. Encouraged, largely, by Mrs Smallholder's extravagant spending habits, the Twig Shop has opened a new branch. The second-hand bookshop has a real rarity on display in the window: one of the very few unsigned copies of Margaret Thatcher's autobiography. Everyone's trying to make an honest dollar, though you wonder just how many passing motorists will squeal to a halt on seeing a newly-erected sign: Last Surgical Supply Shop Before the Motorway.

Down at the Tattoo Parlour there's a 'three for the price of two' offer on nipple piercing this week, though it's conspicuously failed to bring the expected rush of customers. The tourists seem sensibly resistant to the idea of having more holes in their bodies than they had on the day they were born. And the more adventurous locals already sport intriguing collections of piercings - wherever a spare tuck of flesh can be pinched between finger and thumb - and are fast running out of unperforated skin.

Dope Dealer, for example, has rings in his lips, nose, eyebrows and ears; perhaps elsewhere too, who knows? With his inelegantly wasted frame and pierced extremities, he looks like a human piccolo. A light breeze makes him warble disconcertingly; a strong wind can drive him to distraction and force him indoors. If he were ever to consider getting a proper job (an admittedly unlikely scenario) it would take a lot of work to restore his raddled features to any semblance of normality. At the very least he would need to be sanded down, retouched with Polyfilla and given a coat of primer.

Town Drunk, unwisely venturing into the Tattoo Parlour midway through a three-day bender, needed little persuading to have his foreskin pierced. It means that nobody ever occupies an adjacent urinal in the Grievous Bodily Arms, but, looking on the brighter side, he's been offered a Saturday job as a lawn sprinkler.

The young folk of Milltown are keen to get their belly buttons pierced. It takes only five minutes of their time to aggravage strait-laced parents for months. However, for those past the first flush of youth (or whose parents have become inured to their unusual lifestyle choices) the attractions of body art are less obvious. Having decorated themselves with tattoos, rings and studs, what else is there to add? Go-faster stripes? Fins? Aerodynamic spoilers?

Town Drunk sways a little at he gazes at the patchwork of notices displayed in the newsagent's window. He's looking for something like 'Attractive lottery winner seeks intoxicated companion', but all he sees are the usual offers to locate his chakras and reawaken his sensuous self through music and movement.

Milltown boasts a bewildering variety of new-age therapists, plying their arcane trades out of rented rooms. A century ago the town rang with industrial noises of a rather more urgent kind: the clattering of looms and shuttles making conversation, on any meaningful level, almost impossible. It's all very different today, of course. If you stroll around town you can overhear people engaged in less strident pursuits: the whispering of positive affirmations, the quiet repetition of Shamanic mantras ("Om, Shazam, Fandabidozie...") and the soporific tinkling of wind-chimes. Amongst the gibberish you'll hear nuggets of sensible advice: "Yes, yes, but perhaps you should consider just drinking your *own* urine". Entertaining stuff, of course, though it makes conversation, on any meaningful level, almost impossible.

Despite the obvious over-manning - with practitioners outnumbering customers to an almost surreal degree - they all seem to co-exist quite happily. There's no sectarianism here. You don't see the tarot card readers having pitched battles with the past-life regressionists. You don't get the Reichian therapists trying to march down a road occupied by the Zen Buddhists. It's 'live and let live' here in Milltown - except, of course, for the born-again Christians, who see the mere existence of other beliefs as a personal affront. They regard conversion - albeit on a meaningless level - as an ever-present possibility, which is why a smiling zealot can empty any of Milltown's pubs in a matter of seconds.

Facing Charges

It's often said that we don't really appreciate money we don't earn, though you're unlikely to hear this sentiment from the good people at Roofe Leakes, Milltown's foremost estate agent. Having developed the happy knack of generating the maximum amount of money for the minimum of effort - a process honed to perfection during the heady housing boom of the eighties - they came a bit of a cropper when prices plummeted. Indeed, when the country was languishing in recession, one of the few cheering aspects was watching estate agents going broke on a daily basis.

Trade, for those who survived the slump, seems to be on the up. This is one profession that's busy cleaning up its act; these days even Pinocchio could land a job in the estate agency business, writing noncommittal prose for the sales brochures. But if estate agents are no longer allowed to lie - shamelessly, wantonly, from nine to five every day with maybe an hour off for lunch - then what the hell do we need them for?

As Mr Smallholder walks out of the Milltown branch of Roofe Leakes, he feels a tap on his shoulder. "I think you'd better come with me, sir", says PC Rasher, sole representative of Milltown's police force. Mr Smallholder looks him up and down, in some bemusement; he's never seen a policeman in open-toed sandals before. "Not now, sonny", he says. "If you're selling tickets to the Policeman's Ball, just give my secretary a call".

It's the wrong thing to say. Before you can say 'offshore bank account', Mr Smallholder is being frog-marched into Milltown's compact police station and read his rights. Mr Smallholder interrupts PC Rasher's faltering recitation: "Hang on, laddie, the people I ran over were *old*. They'd all had a decent innings. Look, I'm a fair man: I'll *take* some tickets, for God's sake. As many as you've got. Will this be enough? And a little something for yourself... I'm late for a meeting".

It's the wrong thing to say. PC Rasher ignores the proffered wad of notes with as much dignity as he can muster. "You don't seem to realise, sir, that you are in a great deal of trouble. You won't be going *anywhere* for quite some time." Mr Smallholder slaps his forehead with the palm of his hand. "Yes, of course, I understand now. It's not a matter of money, is it? It's about *honour*". He winks, rolls one trouser leg up to the knee and offers an ambiguous handshake.

It's the wrong thing to do. PC Rasher, rapidly running out of patience, produces a charge sheet and licks the end of his pencil. Sensing trouble, Mr Smallholder changes tack once again. "I'm very sorry, officer, I'm under a lot of pressure at work. I'm a very, very busy and successful man. Sometimes I don't realise what I'm doing after I've had a few drinks".

It's the wrong thing to say. Mr Smallholder bites his lip in vexation; he can see his business lunch going the same way as the meeting. He's ushered into the toilet with a small flask to fill and re-emerges, a few minutes later, red-faced and breathless. "Well, I'm glad that's sorted out now", he beams, unctuously. "I'm always happy to be of assistance to our splendid boys in blue. You all do such a marvellous job. But I really have to be off now".

It's the wrong thing to say. Two minutes later Mr Smallholder is sitting disconsolately in a spartan cell, minus his belt and shoe-laces. He feels aggrieved; that half-witted policeman never mentioned anything about a *urine* sample? It was a mistake anyone could make, particularly an over-stressed financier with a lot on his mind and a splendid vintage port sluicing around in his stomach.

Mr Smallholder's diminutive semen sample taxes the skills of the boys down at forensic. They eventually establish that he's twice over the legal limit for alcohol... and even manage to clear up a number of unsolved paternity suits that have been languishing in the files. With PC Rasher being short of time, Mr Smallholder has to write his own confession. It's a sobering moment.

Back at their luxury farmhouse, Mrs Smallholder takes the news of her husband's arrest very hard. She maintains a lonely vigil: reclined on a divan, eating continental chocolates and ordering useless items of frippery from the Shopping Channel. Who would begrudge her the small comfort, during this difficult time, of giving her credit cards some serious hammer?

In between dialling freephone numbers she thinks back, wistfully, to happier times. What had it been about Mr Smallholder that had first attracted her? His rugged good looks? His untarnished credit rating? Or - yes, that was it - his thrilling disregard for financial probity. She recalls, with a sigh, how he'd wooed her with expensive gifts and stock options, finally clinching the marriage deal with a watertight prenuptial agreement.

But their comfortable lifestyle seems to be disintegrating at a startling rate. As she delves into the bottom of the chocolate box for the last nut cluster, Mrs Smallholder idly wonders how her incarcerated husband would react to a quickie divorce. She had promised to stand by him for richer for poorer, in sickness and in health, but there's nothing (even in the small print... and she's already checked) about wasting the best years of her life visiting a disgraced financier in prison. That wasn't the plan at all.

Fools on the Hills

When town-dwellers find the prospect of ploughing through the pile of Sunday papers just too intimidating, and thoughts turn instead to a day in the country, the cry of 'Let's mosey on down to Milltown' seems to have the required alliterative allure to propel couch potatoes off their sofas and into their cars. On sunny weekends the traffic snakes sedately towards Milltown. Visitors are an uncomplaining lot: an hour spent in a traffic jam - with radiators, frazzled parents and bored kids all ready to explode - seems to be an essential ingredient of a good day out.

It's one of life's minor mysteries why 'pay & display' car-parks prove such an irresistible draw to jaded townies. They want to get away to the country - and Milltown is surrounded by some of the finest countryside in the South Pennines - yet no sooner have they reached a 'pay & display' car-park than their courage seems to fail them. Suddenly they become acutely aware of the umbilical cord that binds them, albeit invisibly, to their cars. Perhaps *this* is what makes people descend on

Milltown in such numbers: whatever we've got by way of tourist attractions can be viewed without breaking sweat, or straying more than a few yards from the comforting presence of their cars.

For a lot of visitors to Milltown - raised on the free-market notion that 'you get what you pay for' - the success of a day out can be reckoned by totting up what they've spent. It's a simple calculation. Their pockets are empty by the time they head for home... *ergo*, they must have had a good time.

It's a feeling that our tourism officer is happy to foster. He's also doing his best to attract visitors out of season, and this year's theme is walking. Seasoned hikers need no persuading that Milltown is the ideal base from which to explore the South Pennine hills. But, almost by definition, they tend to be a self-reliant bunch. Instead of throwing their money about in Milltown, they come prepared for every eventuality - with rucksacks full of waterproofs, maps, blister cream, sandwiches and flasks of tea. Within ten minutes of arriving in Milltown, they are just specks disappearing over the first horizon.

For every accomplished hiker, however, there are dozens of people whose walking experience extends no further than a brief expedition down to the corner shop to buy a daily paper and twenty Bensons. People who have never knowingly crossed a contour line. And these are the very people who are currently being wooed by our tourism officer. It's a tactic fraught with pitfalls, as he is just beginning to realise.

They come ill-prepared for a change in the weather, or the ravages of hunger and thirst - assuming, unwisely, that there'll be a take-away over the crest of every hill. The only thing they carry is a little brochure about the newly inaugurated Milltown Way: a splendid ramble that includes some of the area's loveliest landscapes. The proud handiwork of our tourism officer, the brochure offers - in theory, at least - an easily-followed route.

So much for theory. A few disgruntled farmers have tossed the newly-erected waymarking signs over the nearest dry stone wall or - more sneakily - rotated the finger-posts through ninety degrees. The result is a lot of disorientated walkers staring uncomprehendingly at their brochures, holding them first one way and then the other. The only thing they are sure of is that they are hopelessly lost.

This is the moment that panic sets in. The hills that looked so inviting through the windscreen of a speeding car now seem gloomily oppressive. Trees creak and bend alarmingly in a stiffening wind. Storm clouds gather. Grouse take wing with heart-stopping suddenness, their call a mocking 'Go back, go back, go back'.

Groups of terrified walkers empty out their pockets. Some, fearing the worst, are scribbling notes to their loved ones: heartfelt things they wish they had got round to saying much earlier. Others are pooling their meagre resources, wondering how long they might survive by sharing a packet of Cheesy Wotsits and a can of Tizer. One or two are eyeing up their fellow hikers and thinking the unthinkable: if the worst came to the worst, who would they eat first? And then someone cuts through the rising hysteria, produces a mobile phone and says, ingenuously, "Would *this* be any use?" *Any use?* It's a life-saver...

Milltown's hill rescue service is manned by a dedicated crew of men - grizzled Chris Bonnington look-alikes, every one. In the past they've mustered every few weeks to bring an injured walker down from the tops. But now the fells are full of nincompoops with mobile phones, who seem to regard the rescuers as a convenient extension of room service. They have only the vaguest notion of what constitutes an emergency, which is why the rescuers are taking an increasing number of calls requesting they deliver "a new pair of boot-laces" or "some milk for the tea, we forgot to bring any". Some callers don't have a clue where they are: "If we *knew* where we were, we wouldn't be ringing you, would we? We're *lost*, for God's sake. Send a helicopter; it's starting to rain..."

Now it's the turn of Milltown's tourism officer to get a phone-call - from the leader of the hill rescue service. He sits bolt upright in his chair. Our tourism officer isn't accustomed to hearing the kind of language that's surging down the phone-line in a torrent of abuse. When he's able to get a word in edgeways he makes a solemn promise: there'll be no more brochures inviting ill-equipped townies to explore the landscapes around Milltown.

He's true to his word. From now on, visitors to Milltown will be encouraged to resume more familiar pursuits. Like tackling the Milltown Munroes: the aim is to browse around every single craft-shop in town before acute tannin deprivation sets in. Then, wearied by their exertions, they can rest their legs in one of Milltown's many tea-rooms.

Anybody too knackered to lift a cup of tea to parched lips can have it intravenously. After a few platefuls of pikelets, tea-cakes, fruit-scones and - sensibly - some low-calorie cola to wash it all down with, our less adventurous visitors can justifiably feel they've enjoyed the very best that Milltown has to offer.

Passion Play

It's high summer, the traditional 'silly season', when politicians decamp, en masse, to deepest Tuscany, to enjoy a little rest and recreation before the resumption of hostilities. Here in Milltown we have a silly season of our own, when a paucity of hard news makes the editor of the *Milltown Times* search - in vain - for meaningful stories. The only significant noise emanating from the newspaper's compact office is the unmistakable sound of a barrel being scraped.

So the paper has been happy to proclaim the news of the Milltown Miracle far beyond this valley, with the result that our church has joined Mecca, Knock and Lords as a holy place of pilgrimage. People are coming from far and wide to gaze in wonderment at the weeping effigy of St Diana, Our Lady of the Landmines. The miracle even made the cover of *Which Altarboy* magazine: reckoned to be the highest accolade in ecclesiastical circles. The Vicar of Milltown ought to be gratified to see so many eager supplicants packed into his church... but he's not.

He bites his lip; he knows only too well that he's supped with the Devil. In fact he's not merely supped with the Devil, but has cheerfully gone all the way with the horned one, doing things of a frankly sexual nature which even Mrs Satan - generally reckoned to be broad-minded and unshockable - would blanch at. It's only a matter of time before our vicar is unmasked as a charlatan, and the weeping figure of St Diana as a blatant fake. But the further he walks down the perfumed road towards the eternal bonfire, the harder it is to find his way back to the path of righteousness.

At the risk of being churlish, there are people - yes, even here in Milltown - who can put Princess Diana's accomplishments into sharp perspective. Carers who continue to hold the hands of Aids patients, even after the film-crews have yelled "Cut, it's a wrap" and put the lens caps back on their cameras. Yes, nurses. And let's tip our caps to the unsung heroes whose job it is to disable those accursed landmines: men for whom a minefield represents a traumatic day's work and not merely another photo-opportunity.

These are just the kind of men that Wounded Man is hoping to emulate. Men of action. Men who react to the prospect of danger with courage and self-reliance. Men who are happy to take on whole battalions single-handedly, armed only with a snarl, a sweaty singlet and a Bowie knife. Down from Wounded Man's bedroom wall come the inspirational pictures of Mahatma Ghandi and Florence Nightingale; up go posters of of Arnie Swarzenegger and Sylvester Stallone, armed to the teeth. More appropriate role models for a man facing his mid-life crisis.

Wounded Man is fed up with being a good listener. The trouble with listening empathetically to other peoples' problems is that you can end up doing it rather too much of the time. Given a choice in the matter he'd rather be the Man With No Name: a charismatic stranger with a steely gaze and a monosyllabic line in conversation, who rides into a troubled little town and is persuaded to tackle the bad guys. The result is a foregone conclusion: the desperados are no match for the stranger's vengeance. It's simple, eye-for-an-eye, Old Testament stuff. By the time he's finished there are bandits, dead as doornails, strewn all over the place... though the townsfolk discover that justice exacts a high price.

Like an avenging angel, the stranger forces the menfolk to confront their numerous inadequacies. The menfolk, on the other hand, would prefer to leave their inadequacies just where they are: out of sight, swept quietly under the carpet. One by one the women of the town overcome their reluctance to sleep with a man who hasn't showered for six months. Best of all, the Man With No Name doesn't sit impassively at a stripped pine kitchen table, listening to their interminable grumbles. He gives each one a Damn Good Shagging instead, which (this is movie-land, remember...) magically transforms raving harpies into compliant, doe-eyed maidens. When he leaves them, their hair is spread out over the pillow and there's a dreamy, far-away look in their eyes.

The Man With No Name doesn't think: "Hmmm, Deadman's Gulch... not a bad little place. Maybe it's time to settle down, find myself a bride and start up a business. This town looks like it could do with a decent dry goods store". He doesn't start looking at houses, or mulling over the pros and cons of simple repayment schemes and endowment mortgages. No, he just saddles up his horse and rides off into the sunset.

Apart from the undertaker - who reckons that Christmas has come early this year - the men are damn glad to see the stranger go. He may have saved them from the hoodlums, but life in Deadman's Gulch will never be the same again. The men know they've been compared to the Man With No Name... and have come off badly in every respect. The women part their curtains to watch the stranger ride down Main Street one last time. They smile their secret smiles. Having tasted the forbidden fruit of unbridled passion with a *real* man, there's nothing to suggest that they'll be content to go back to their husbands and an unchanging diet of apple pie.

The Man With No Name: what a guy... He can dispatch the bandits with casual insouciance and a smoking gun. Then, with the same unerring aim - and without even pausing to wash his hands - he can move a woman to the very core of her being. He doesn't talk about it... he just *does* it.

These are thrillingly subversive thoughts for Wounded Man, a good-hearted fellow repressed by years of politeness and political correctness. But good sex *isn't* PC and it isn't polite. Once you start holding open the door that leads to sexual ecstasy ("After you...". "No, after *you*...".) the passion soon gets lost amongst the pleasantries.

Life in the Bus Lane

In a society that seems to deride the wisdom of age and worship the cult of youth, it's heartening to find that Arthur and Martha Fustian, Milltown's oldest hippy settlers, enjoy the respect their longevity deserves. Theirs, after all, was the first covered wagon to head west, in search of freedom, opportunity and an unlimited supply of recreational drugs.

Despite coming in peace, they weren't initially welcomed with open arms. Suspicious locals eyed their loons, Afghan coats and three-button tie-dye T-shirts and came to predictable conclusions about the incomers' moral depravity. The Milltown of old - the Milltown that all but died - had been a place of stolid industry. It was spinning, weaving, cloth-making and millstone grit (rather than face-painting and fortune-telling) that had transformed a swampy river-crossing into a bustling town. So it was perhaps understandable that the locals, dispirited by industrial decline, should have had qualms about those first hippy settlers. The locals' antipathy only began to fade once they realised that the hippies weren't after their jobs. Hardly surprising, really, since there were hardly any jobs to be had.

Life was very different during the 1970s. Milltown was a town in decline; for years it had been a point of departure rather than a destination. So we should give thanks to Arthur and Martha for being the first to see a viable future in a small, defeated Pennine town.

From their damp squat in one of Milltown's empty terraces, Arthur and Martha wrote long letters to friends. They extolled the pleasures of life in Milltown and expressed their hopes for the future. They wanted their enthusiasm to be contagious, thereby encouraging more people to join them in making the town their home. So who can blame them if they occasionally lapsed into imaginative hyperbole?

The recipients of these letters - mostly hapless city folk stuck in dead-end jobs - were entranced by their visions of a better life, and wanted to believe every word. They read avidly: about the friendly locals, the balmy climate, the mild winters, the cheap and plentiful drugs ("A quid deal... as big as a *shoe-box*... Wow!"). They were amazed to read that little 'top & bottom' houses could be bought for a song; this, at least, was incontrovertibly true.

One by one they visited Milltown, to check the place out for themselves and to sleep on Arthur and Martha's floor. Some came for a long weekend, were seduced by the scent of incense and patchouli oil... and never went back. They were quick to forgive Arthur and Martha for their wilder flights of fancy; if Milltown wasn't quite as Utopian as it had been painted, it certainly looked promising. Here was a place where they might be able to make a living, of sorts, by harnessing their rudimentary skills: stringing beads and constructing nail-and-string pictures. Where they could establish complex family dynasties through a combination of casual bed-hopping and drunken forgetfulness. Where, after years of wandering in an urban wilderness, they could find a place that felt like home.

Arthur and Martha are celebrating their ruby wedding anniversary... at least they would be if they had ever bothered to plight their troth in the sight of anyone other than a troupe of shamanic nomads. They are surrounded, on their special day, by all the members of their extended family. From the size of the gathering it seems that most of Milltown can claim Arthur and Martha as antecedents. On arthritic knees they bounce their youngest grandchildren (Three and Four: crazy names, crazy kids...) and regale them with bitter-sweet reminiscences about the good old days. Innocent times when dope dealing was a more gentlemanly pursuit than it is today, and Aids was merely a popular brand of slimming products.

Martha is prompted to recall how Arthur had won her heart, all those years ago. "Well, I've never admitted this to anyone", she blushes, girlishly, "but the truth is that it was *me* who made the running". "So what *did* you say to him, grandma?" Martha, misty-eyed at the memory, reaches for Arthur's hand and gives it a reassuring squeeze. "I said 'Whatever bizarre and degrading act you've *ever* wanted to do with a woman... well I *am* that woman'. And then I hid his clothes...".

"Well, Arthur", says Wounded Man, toasting the happy couple with a glass of elderberry wine, "you've had a long life, fathered many children and witnessed some of the most important events and developments of the century. If you could have your time over again, is there anything you would change?" Arthur strokes his chin and takes some time to reflect; a lifetime of substance abuse has left him a little hard of thinking. "Well, yes", he answers, slowly, "I guess I'd like to have seen more women naked."

On the Edge

Even with a poncho, a sunbed tan and a week's growth of stubble, Wounded Man bears scant resemblance to The Man With No Name. He just looks like old man Steptoe in a blanket. But there's no going back - not once he's sniffed the cordite in the air. He craves danger, excitement and adventure. He wants to pit himself against incalculable odds - a need unsatisfied by the weekly lottery draw. Even Triple Stamp Week down at the Co-op fails to quicken the pulse like it used to do.

He's made a start, of sorts, in adopting an outlaw lifestyle: there are overdue library books scattered all over his little house. Is he going to take them back to the library? Is he buggery... When he gets a stroppy letter from the bank informing him that his account "appears to be overdrawn", Wounded Man doesn't merely resort to cringing and begging: his usual response in the face of financial adversity. He has the presence of mind, instead, to compose a playfully flippant reply: "Feel free to write me again when you're absolutely sure". He's already walked into his bank manager's office, armed only with a few good intentions and some hastily-concocted - and totally irrelevant - figures jotted down on the back of an envelope. Now *that's* scary.

When a lady with a clipboard full of stupid questions stops him in the street, Wounded Man gives in to his rebellious instincts. He tells her a blatant lie - about his age - only to find her writing the figure down without comment. It's liberating, for a hitherto law-abiding man, to realise not merely that he can lie... but that he can lie openly and often, *and* get away with it.

He's emboldened to tell a few more gratuitous porkies, just for the hell of it. "Height?" 7ft... "Employment?" Rocket scientist... "Favourite food?" Turnip... It's exciting to imagine that some frozen food conglomerate will be encouraged to introduce some appalling new product ('Turnip Surprise: tiny baby turnips marinaded in a spicy Chinese-style sauce, ready to microwave in seconds'), based solely on the barefaced lies that people like Wounded Man have told to middle-aged women carrying clipboards.

Every Thursday evening a group of unfulfilled men congregates in a draughty hall, ostensibly to rediscover their virility. It's a quality that seems to have shrivelled, alarmingly, like Wounded Man's scrotum after a cold shower. Within the supportive atmosphere of the Milltown Men's Group they try to undo some of the bad habits to which men have unwittingly subscribed.

There's Domesticity Avoidance. "That's it", says the group leader encouragingly, "you fill the sink up with hot water, put all the pots in... and just leave them there, 'to soak'. *For how long?* What sort of question is *that?*"

"And what's *this?*" says the leader, waving an electric iron above his head. He is met with blank, uncomprehending stares from all corners of the room. "Excellent", he beams, with the air of a man whose message is beginning to hit home.

Then there's poetry. For *real* men? Yes, indeed... The leader assures the group that poetry *can* be both accessible and bereft of meaning. To prove his point he plays a tape of that most comforting of mantras: James Alexander Gordon reading the football results. There's hardly a dry eye in the house when he comes to that most mellifluous and alliterative of Scottish score-lines: "East Fife 4, Forfar 5". It's powerful medicine for men who've lost the sporting habit: a shipping forecast for the landlocked, a weather forecast for the housebound, a Lord's Prayer for the Godless...

One group member raises his hand, shyly. "Ah, you want some advice about women", says the leader, tapping the side of his nose and winking broadly. "Well, that's too big a subject to cover in one evening, so I'll just leave you with a simple chat-up line to experiment with. I think you'll find that a combination of honesty, condescension and naked lust can often work wonders. Something like this: 'I'm not just interested in your tits, love, I'm interested in *all* your erogenous zones'... Give it a try and report back next week."

That's enough talk; it's time for a hands-on demonstration of male culinary skills. What *is* it about men and barbecues? Once they've had three sunny days in a row, even men who'd baulk at grilling toast will happily haul a rusty barbecue out into the front yard, fill it with charcoal, pour on half a can of petrol... and, with never a thought for their own safety, casually toss a match in. Then, once they've beaten back the flames, they add some steaks (a good idea...) or maybe just a catering pack of budget beef-burgers (not so good...). Perhaps the smell of incinerated meat is a potent folk-memory from long ago: times when men dressed in fur, communicated in guttural grunts and treated their women like chattels. That's right, the sixties...

The whole barbecue scene doesn't play so well with women. Do *they* get extravagant praise for cremating cheap cuts of meat? No, they just get another pile of washing-up to do, while their partners are doing a drunken lap of honour with a tray of charred sausages.

View to the Bridge

It's official: the lottery has overtaken the weather as the nation's favourite topic of conversation. "I hear that ball number nine has been picked out no fewer than sixty-eight times. *Sixty-eight times!* That's pretty amazing, isn't it? Yeah, looks like rain again. Summer? We haven't *had* a summer. Well, not a summer to speak of. At this rate it'll soon be Christmas. Oh God, I think my brain's burst...".

Wounded Man takes a break from lottery madness and his halting attempts at self-improvement. Feeling the need for some fresh air, he climbs a steep flight of old stone steps, each one deeply dished from long use. Within minutes he emerges, breathless, onto the breezy tops above Milltown, to find the heather in bloom and a lark in song. The swallows are mustering on the telephone wires, preparing for their long flight south. The sun, as it gets lower in the sky, becomes a blood-red ball. It's late afternoon in late summer: exactly a year, to the day, since Princess Diana entered a dark tunnel and emerged into the light.

From a thoughtfully sited bench Wounded Man enjoys a panoramic view of the town: a compact huddle of old stone houses tightly shoe-horned into the valley below. The rows of terraced 'top and bottom' houses may at this very moment be witnessing all kinds of family dramas, but from a distance the town seems hushed and serene. The only noise that disturbs the stillness comes from the church far below; the organist is doodling on a theme that sounds suspiciously like Candle in the Wind.

As he surveys the town, Wounded Man is in reflective mood. It seems to get harder and harder to hear the silence through the crackle and static of everyday life. We rush through life as though it were a race, hardly daring to stop, look and listen, in case - gulp - we discover we've wasted our best years doing something monumentally pointless, like being an estate agent.

Our time-saving devices would make more sense if we actually did something useful with all the time we save. We eat on the hoof, like grazing ruminants, in order to stockpile a few precious seconds... only to spend a fruitless hour stalled in a traffic snarl-up. It doesn't make much sense.

We seem happy to collude in the tawdry conspiracy to make us more stupid. We're disorientated: dazzled by the lights of the marketing juggernaut. "Here I am", we seem to be saying, "rip me off". When he caught, by accident, a particularly unpleasant episode of the Jerry Springer Show ("I'll do anything... and I mean *anything*... to get on TV"), Wounded Man was mesmerised by what he saw. If there really *is* a conspiracy, then it looks to be well on schedule.

It's baffling. Whenever we are offered a free choice between something that's meaningful, resonant and *real*... and something that's utterly bogus... why do we inexorably plump for the latter? It is tempting to hope, as we approach a new millennium, that we'll be searching, in ever greater numbers, for that elusive quality of authen-ticity in our lives. It's tempting... but Wounded Man won't be betting his last fiver on the possibility.

He gazes down on a town in miniature: a town that saw its principal industries wither away, yet somehow managed to overcome the trauma. At one time there were more than thirty mill chimneys belching smoke into the valley, and the rocky gritstone outcrops that overlook the town are still blackened by smoke and soot. We can mourn the buildings that were thoughtlessly lost to the bulldozers and wrecking balls - during the sixties, when Milltown's industrial past wasn't reckoned to have much of a part to play in Milltown's future. Equally, we can give thanks that so much of the town *did* survive the planners' blitzkrieg.

Milltown, being wedged into a fold in the hills, had no room to expand. There's no suburban sprawl: no prim housing estates where they chop down all the trees, then thoughtfully name the roads after them. Just a few cramped streets - peopled by an intriguing cast of characters. A cast that's grown in numbers since Arthur and Martha first put down roots here a quarter of a century ago. And, God knows, a lot of water has flowed under the old packhorse bridge since then.

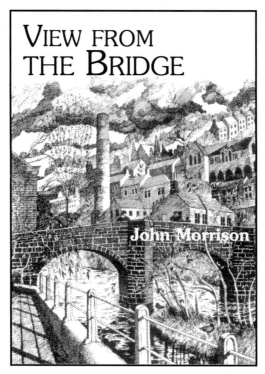

VIEW FROM THE BRIDGE

John Morrison

View From the Bridge is an affectionately jaundiced view of Milltown, a place not unlike Hebden Bridge. When this little old milltown went into serious decline, it soon filled up again with an intriguingly diverse cast of 'off-cumdens'. Artists, writers, ne'er-do-wells, new-age therapists, lovers, loners and losers: people who've mulled over life's great questions and who must now admit that, no, they still don't know the way to San José.

Sales boomed once the local press had banned all mention of the book. The editors seemed to identify disturbingly quickly with a mildly unflattering pen-portrait of a fictional newspaper. Yes, if you hold up a distorting mirror to a small community, it's amazing how many people will imagine themselves to be reflected in it.

See the latest episodes at **http://www.hebdenbridge.co.uk**
Details of all Pennine Pens publications and
our **Web Design** services are on the Internet at
http://www.penpens.demon.co.uk

Other books from Pennine Pens

A Little Bridge by Debjani Chatterjee,
Basir Sultan Kazmi and Simon Fletcher

(£5.95 and 95p p&p)

The Chess Board by Basir Sultan Kazmi

(£4.95 and 95p p&p)

The Occasions of Love by Simon Fletcher

(£4.95 and 95p p&p)

Audio book version   (£4.95 and 95p p&p)

Me, Mick and M31 by Andrew Bibby
Children's environmental mystery (£5.95 and 95p p&p)

Sylvia Plath: Killing the Angel in the House
by Elaine Connell   (£7.95 and 95p p&p)
A very readable introduction to the works of this great poet.
Second edition with new preface available Autumn 1998

Presenting the Past: Anne Lister of Halifax
Jill Liddington   (£5.95 and 95p p&p)
19th century lesbian landowner, traveller and diarist.

Cycling in Search of the Cathars
Chris Ratcliffe and Elaine Connell (£7.95 and 65p p&p)
This book about the "heretics" of medieval southwest France is
currently out of print. A full colour digital version is, however,
available for the Mac or PC - CD or floppy.

Asma's Egg
Words: Chris Ratcliffe. Illustrations: Sean Creagh
For children 4-7   (£1.95 and 45p p&p)

Pennine Pens, 32, Windsor Road, Hebden Bridge,
West Yorkshire, HX7 8LF. Tel/Fax 01422-843724
http://www.penpens.demon.co.uk